ENGAGED YOGA
Yoga woven into daily life

ENGAGED YOGA
Yoga woven into daily life

Siddha Publishing

Order this book at www.siddhapublishing.com

Author: Christopher Gladwell
Editors: Louise Wender and Christopher Gladwell
Design: Ambrose Gladwell
Photographer: Louise Wender

ISBN: 978-0-9567922-4-2

Published by

Siddha Publishing

www.siddhapublishing.com

WITH GRATITUDE

To all our teachers, all our lovers, and all our friends with sublime thanks.

To all the beautiful beings in our lives without whom life would be short of love.

To all of you who have helped us create this book by appearing in the images.

To all our beautiful children, who are the future, may you shine.

Contents

How to use this book

There are eight sections in this book. Each section is divided into a number of chapters, within which you will find teachings, questions, practical meditations, and reflections.

Reflections and meditations can be identified by a vertical orange line, and in italic font.

Questions can be identified by an italic purple font

You can read this book from the beginning, cover to cover. Or you may wish to dip in and out of the texts, browse the images, or focus on the meditations and reflections.

However you choose to enjoy this book we trust that it will bring you much benefit, insight, and joy, and that it will be of benefit to all beings everywhere.

We are building a global Engaged Yoga community and invite you join us. Please get in touch to share your insights and feedback. You can find us at Engaged Yoga on Facebook or through our websites. We look forward to engaging with you.

YOGA
COMING OFF THE MAT

Yoga is so much more than just making shapes on a mat, isn't it?

If yoga is just making shapes on a mat, either a random or very ordered flurry of shapes in space and time, then is it simply a form of ethnic gymnastics?

Let's look a little more deeply.

The fascia of the body are the wrapping layers around the internal structures that both join and separate all the organs, muscles, nerves, blood vessels and so on. When we start to look deeper into the fascial structure of the body we find internal lines of connection and flow that are being released, opened, and energised through the process of working with an intelligent asana practice.

These lines, when energised with breath and the mind's attention, lead towards making the body conscious. Feeling the capacity to switch on and switch off muscle groups at will when flowing from one 'shape' to another also facilitates this creation of what we love to call 'conscious flesh'.

An intelligent asana practice also has bio-mechanically sound alignment. Some body negative systems of yoga ignore alignment and this can and often does lead to physical damage and injury. Love flowing wisely through the body in asana flows in bio-mechanically sound alignment. Anything else is violence to the body, or some form of self-harm.

Superstition is common in what is often called 'traditional' practice. In many cases the word 'traditional' is used as a term to control inquiry, it means 'be quiet and don't ask questions' because 'they' (whoever they are) know better than you.

Of course, if they do know better than you, they can offer very sound rationale and clear evidence for their teachings not based in superstition, hyperbole, hearsay, dogma or confusion.

And if they cant?
Look elsewhere?

We can ascribe all sorts of meanings to the particular shapes we make and why they are better than other shapes. We could also ascribe all sorts of meanings to the particular order of shapes we make and why they are better than another order. Again, how much does this meaning making stand up to real scrutiny?

There is much more we could look at here in terms of the rationale behind the sequencing of asanas and the effects on the mind and so on, but that is not the topic of this book, valuable though such understanding is in terms of taking yoga off the mat.

Already we start to have a system of understanding the physical practices in a way that lifts the practice out of mere ethnic gymnastics into a developmental system. This developmental system uses the body as one aspect of the experience of incarnation that is available to the processes of awareness. A physical practice is really an awareness practice; remember, it is making the flesh conscious.

An authentic yoga practice is working towards understanding the inseparable flow of life as body, feeling, bio-energy, mind, vibration, ecology and deep sentience. Anything less is a partial practice.

When we begin to understand the real nature of inseparability, we have no alternative but to take the practice off the mat into daily life.

How does this work though?

What does it actually mean to take the practice into daily life?

Many people talk about compassion and being compassionate in daily life towards others. But what does this really mean?

It is often understood as being sweet to everyone, making sure no-one's feelings get ruffled and helping everyone to feel good about themselves.

Really this can be collusion with someone's egoic position. If we are not in a fully awakened state ourselves we may not be ready to work with the reality of compassion, or even love. We can always practice simple kindness, kindness itself is more than good enough.

When we are fully awakened beyond the illusions of our own self-story creation, then we can begin to comprehend compassion and love. Compassion is ultimately facilitating the transparency of the self-story mechanism in all beings everywhere. This dissolution of the self-story mechanism through it becoming transparent leads to the ultimate freedom of yoga. It is from this place of freedom that one can then live as love through responsive, creative and spontaneously appropriate action.

> *Facilitating someone else's ego story is not ultimate compassion, it is collusion with the illusion of him or her being a somebody, a separate self. So what often passes as compassion is in fact detrimental to deeper development and can potentially be just ego-massage.*

So what to do?

How about acting with simple kindness whilst practicing' towards ultimate compassion and love?

In this way, compassion and love eventually flows by itself.

Authentic yoga really begins to evidence itself when you realise the relationship between your practice and your actions and words in your daily life, in your workplace, in your home-life and with your friends, family and people that you feel challenged by. Yoga really begins to grow when taken off the mat or meditation cushion.

Authentic yoga really does begin with paying attention to the nature of inseparability. The way we do this is to start behaving as if everything were inseparable. The word often used in Sanskrit teaching to describe inseparability is Brahman.

Whenever you come across this word you could usefully translate it as 'inseparability'.

tIf you really knew that you were inseparable from everything else, how might you behave?

Might you show every thing respect?

Could you honour all the movements and flows of energy and treat everything with appreciation?

How might you be aware of all the ways that things are always and already connected, and through this process then choose to be attentive, loving and kind to all beings everywhere?

And so the paradox arises.

How do you sustain incarnation without harming other beings from which you are, on some level or another, inseparable?

How will you eat well and treat your own existence with kindness, love and respect whilst deeply computing that to stay alive and well you have to consume life-form?

How will you deal with the simple fact that all of life is sacred and yet every incarnate being will almost certainly terminate?

We will die, you will die, everything will die in its incarnate form, how will you face this, honour this and process this?

Authentic yoga addresses these paradoxical positions from the very beginning. Even though the levels of realisation available to a beginner are not sufficient to handle such paradox, the methods of practice offer a way of exploring this.

The beginning of any authentic yoga practice certainly contains what I'm going to call 'pragmatic ethics'.

Ethics in yoga is utterly pragmatic, it is not some system of philosophical debate about right and wrong. Yogic ethics begins with the recognition of inseparability. It works from this premise and encourages this realisation.

From the beginning we are invited to behave in ways that pay attention to the inseparable nature of reality, so that as we practice our perspective itself is being led deeper into this realisation, into deep recognition and remembrance of the nature of Brahman.

When we embody the inter-relatedness of all sentient living beings, and even recognise all of life as being potentially sentient, this is the reality of engaging with utterly inter-connected flow. Yoga does not need to teach dogma, it doesn't matter if everything is sentient or not because if we behave as if it were, our behaviour is altered from when we treat everything as a resource merely to be used or abused at our will.

> *So if you try practising as if everything in your world had some level of sentience and was to be treated with respect, how would that affect the way you are with the flow of phenomena that is your life?*

Certainly we can begin practice, we can do cleansing practices and we can practice some asana. However, the beginning of this realisation of the total inter-relatedness of all life and the supports of life has to preface deeper practice, so it is that we engage in pragmatic ethics.

If this recognition of inseparability is not effectively embodied, then all the practices we do remain an affair of the ego, a narcissistic dance of self-aggrandisement and the building of the self-story. Enlightened self-interest is not enough in the world of authentic yoga other than as a very basic building block to deeper practice.

The realisation of inter-dependence is the essential framework underlying the ethical foundation of all yogic developmental practices. As such, the practice of yogic ethics is a profound practice in its own right.

The pragmatic ethics of yoga will inexorably deepen you in this realisation of inter-dependence and inseparability.

This realisation of inter-dependence is the second step in establishing the foundations of practice. The first step recognises and then realises what we can call impermanence.

Impermanence is simply the fact that every apparently separate thing terminates at some point or another. This step itself takes us into really understanding the systemic nature of reality, the ecological reality in which we find ourselves. We will terminate carrots as we grate them into our healthy raw food salads and transform them into our flesh, excrement, and, after we die, into the flesh of worms!

There is no part of our physical, energetic or mental existence that is not dependent on and ultimately inter-dependent with all other aspects of the flow that is life. There is no part of our living experience that is not co-arising with apparently separate life-forms in some way or another.

This is a crucial point and one worth reading over and over until it is deeply understood and starts to percolate into your cells.

We know that there is no part of our physical being that is not dependent on the earth and its minerals, no part of our physical being that is not dependent on the oceans, rivers and waters of this planet as well as the air. We know that there is no part of our physical being that is not dependent on the sunlight that has nourished all of life on this planet. We know that the amazingly diverse lifeforms that inhabit this planet are all part of the one beautifully complex system that is the biosphere.

All of the component parts of this biosphere are equally valuable, we are just one of these parts, dependent on the whole, and never separate from the ecology of our planet as it is our life support system, it is 'us'.

No, we have no choice if we are to live with integrity
but to take our practice off the mat or cushion.

Physically we depended on our parents, families or other primary carers. Others may depend on us in a similar way, such is the inter-dependence of our own species.

We are also inter-dependent as an integral part of the political, social and financial systems that provide food and water, carry away and process our wastes, and on the social systems that provide services such as education, health care and so on.

Emotionally we are in relationship with those who love us and those we love, and we have learnt how to experience, process and share our emotions from significant people in our

lives, usually our parents or therapists!

Cognitively we are in an inter-dependent relationship with all those whose ideas have ever inspired us and whom we inspire. The syntheses and creations of our minds are inter-dependent with those who have helped and continue to help feed our minds, as we also may help nourish other minds.

A bee cannot exist without a flower, a flower cannot exist without a bee. For the evolution of flowering plants, pollinating insects had to co-evolve. For the evolution of pollinating insects, flowers too had to co-evolve. Co-evolution is the co-arising flow of inter-dependence. Nothing is a separate inherent thing, the bee is flow, the flower is flow, both together flow. Evolution is, in reality, a deliciously complex web of co-evolution. Not only is everything inter-dependent but also arises as inter-dependence. We are inter-dependence. That's worth repeating, we are inter-dependence.

So here we have it, yogic ethics is a practice as well as providing guidelines to practice. Yogic ethics creates the framework from which we understand practice and from which we can then realise inter-dependence.

Without such a code of ethical practice, it can be virtually impossible to realise inter-dependence in an embodied way. Without such an embodied realisation there is no practice, no real yoga can occur, only aggrandisement and gratification of the separate self-construct and from here enlightened self-interest. No matter how shiny it may be, this is not enough!

Remember, practice really is remembrance, it is another opportunity to recognise our true and original nature. Our true nature is deeper than the illusion of the separate self-sense. Our original nature is found through the unfolding of this dualistic contraction, this self-sense that in yoga is usually called 'ego' or in Sanskrit 'Ahamkara'.

Perhaps we could extend our study by looking at Jain Yoga, Sikh Yoga and Buddhist Yoga and explore the ethical frameworks from these traditions?

Perhaps we can look at the ethical framework of Christianity as a form of Yoga and also from Humanist traditions and look for similarities in scope and rationale?

Such study is eminently worthy.

Some traditions might suggest that if you misbehave you won't go to heaven.

Some traditions offer a sort of 'do as you would be done by' rationale.

Some traditions say that 'what goes around comes around'.

Some just consider it to be more evolved to treat other beings with kindness and respect.

As a contemporary yoga practitioner why would you practice ethics?

What practices would you pay attention to and why?

CONTEMPORARY ETHICS

The pragmatics of ethics

When we look into the history of Yoga we find a range of related versions of ethical practices that anyone taking the path of Yoga would have some acquaintance with. Any authentic practitioner would at some point in their training be faced with a series of practices that we could call ethical codes, observations or requirements.

It is the view being posited here that these codes are actually initially selfish. They are a pragmatic system to boundary the ego of the practitioner. They do this through crafting a ring-fence of codes that prevent the practitioner from turning the practices into fuel for a bigger and shinier self-story.

In Patanjali's Yoga Sutras written around the year 200c.e. we find yogic ethics described in terms of the Yamas and Niyamas. These ethical codes are essentially unattainable, in our view they are not dogma, not rules to live by, but are paths to realisation and awakening.

People so often use ethical guidelines as dogmatic rules with which to beat others and themselves with. In our understanding of yoga as a science of the direct experience of reality, as a technology of subjectivity and as a method of ecstatic and blissful living, such dogmatic sadism and masochism is a phase to move through as quickly as possible.

Yoga as a science of direct experience is a system of methods. These methods are a synergy of approaches that have evolved to cultivate the direct experience of reality. An ethical frame-work of practice, such as the yamas and niyamas, are methods to confine the self-sense and assist all the other methods of practice to function. The function of all the methods of practice is to realise their goals of the realisation of inseparability, embodied knowing of one's original nature,t and ecstatic awakening to the the continuum of bliss, pure being and awareness as the ineffable structure of mundane everyday life.

The self-sense, the ego, confined in the paradoxical and unattainable parameters of pragmatic ethics gradually becomes transparent in its machinations. As it squirms about in desperation to survive as the top dog, the CEO of the Universe, it becomes boring in its observable pathological parody. Its tedious control strategies as it seeks to box phenomena and keep them safe, as it seeks to generate only experiences that gratify and satisfy its story and as it perpetuates the insanity of the solidity of the separate self utterly divided from the 'other' in a tragic facsimile of love, all become visible.

The unattainable parameters of the pragmatic ethics gradually lead to the dissolution of the ego as the driving force in life, they dismiss the ego as the CEO and open up the post to one's original nature, to what many call Buddha-nature, Brahman, the Divine or some such title.

Upon realisation of inseparability, upon embodied knowing of divinity (or pure-being-ness) and the remembrance of this as one's core-identity, then the self-sense, the ego, is relegated to its proper function. This is simply to channel and open the ways for pure being-ness to pour its gifts onto the planet through the dance of the no longer separate flow of integral unicity. No ego-dectomy is required!

Without these practices in place, yoga so easily ends up as a sort of ridiculous competitive narcissism that completely fails to comprehend even the basics of reality as it is.

One does not have to look too far to see this sort of distorted pseudo-yogic behaviour. There are hot styles and eminent teachers of this style who display massively un-yogic behaviour. There are practitioners of capability-oriented asana series that display equally undeveloped behaviour. There are thousands of folk bending themselves backwards and forwards in 'Hindu aerobics' classes trying to look 'fitter' and be 'shinier' than the separate body next to them. There are also teachers of what they call 'awakening' that is really no more than enlightened self-interest. This neurotic and narcissistic behaviour sadly limits this awesome developmental discipline to a game of ego dynamics.

We want you to want so much more than this!
Will you?

Yamas are really codes of practice that act to restrain behaviours that arise out of the ignorance of separation. The experience of feeling like a separate self-thing moves through several forms of behaviour.

It moves through ignorant indifference manifesting as thoughts, feelings and behaviours of "I dont care" or "It doesn't matter to me".

It moves through unhealthy craving, the feeling that you can only be happy or complete if you have this thing. This energy grows into greed.

It moves through fear and withdrawal, maybe not speaking the truth when it is needed and certainly not behaving with truth and clarity when it is needed, it is a pulling away in fear.

It moves in envy, jealousy and hatred. All these behaviours arise out of feeling a lack, a sense of being less than and how someone else has something that would make you full or complete. Hatred is simply not seeing that everything is connected. In hating you are deluded as to the nature of reality. So the Yamas also act as a restraint to the behaviours arising from delusion.

The primary Yama is called Ahimsa and most simply means non-harming. Ahimsa is beautifully impossible! Ahimsa is a method to explore the relationship to all other apparently separate lifeforms. Ahimsa is a means to discover certain aspects of reality. If you try to take ahimsa to extremes you will still fail, you may break the legs of ants as you brush them out of your way, you may starve yourself to death if you seek to avoid killing any living cells, or you may (as one of Christopher's teachers put it) consume homeopathic quantities of field mouse or beetle in your daily bread or sunflower seeds, you will certainly consume millions of living protozoa in every mouthful of water, consigning the majority of them to certain death in the acid environment of your stomach. Your immune system will murder trillions of micro-organisms all seeking to make a home or dinner out of your form. Whichever way, from any intelligent perspective you will recognise that you can only fail at ahimsa.

Don't miss the point though. These ethical codes are not meant for unconscious literal interpretation but conscious involvement in practice and the recognition that they are ultimately impossible. Recognising that impossibility, we practice anyway and as we practice we understand the apparently paradoxical relationship between the sacredness of all life and the sacrifice of all apparently separate life-form back into the appearance of dissolution. We get to practically feel and understand the many as the One and the One as the many.

Satya is the second of the Yamas in Patanjali's offering. Satya literally means unchangeable, the constancy that is all pervasive. Satya is that which is true and real in the cosmos whilst Satyam literally means truthfulness, one is full with this truth.

The practice of satya or satyam is to speak from this place of cosmic constancy, which requires one to pay attention to one's speech. Are you speaking from a place of deep integrity or just trying to win, prove a point, or achieve some goal based on your sense of being separate?

From a place of feeling separate, hearing truth can feel overly challenging, in fact it can feel brutal. So the truth has to be balanced with ahimsa.

There are many practices of communication that are profound and one of these is Marshall Rosenberg's Non-Violent-Communication. This separates out judgements from the mix of communication and frees up one's thoughts and words to be more reflective and kinder. Ahimsa is always balanced with truthing. These two practices are two sides of the same coin and support and enhance each other in a mutually developing dance of attention and feeling.

Niyamas are observances that tend to create a more happy and healthy engagement with life. Again there are many ways of interpreting these observances from the more fundamental to the more utilitarian and libertarian. Since fundamentalism rarely leads to real happiness for anyone we will head to the more libertarian interpretations.

Santosha is the second Niyama, santosha is sublime contentment with every arising phenomenon. Santosha relieves the desire to grasp, hoard and acquire. It suggests a natural, already existent perfection that requires no change or transformation.

Tapas as the third Niyama is the disciplined application of effort for the purposes of transformation. Literally it translates as 'heat'. We also like to understand its deeper meaning as extending to one's edges with consciousness for the purposes of development.

These two practices of Santosha and Tapas immediately appear to be paradoxical demands.

Aren't these two practices clearly incompatible with each other? How can you possibly practice appropriate diligent effort for transformation and complete acceptance and joy with every arising phenomenon, as it is, without wanting anything to be any different, together?
How can you possibly practice these two at the same time?

You have to cultivate comfort and ease with paradox. You have to relax into paradox. This is part of the path of continuous realisation, part of the path of beginning-less and eternal evolutionary enlightenment, which is of course one of the keys to real freedom, the liberation that all authentic Yogic teachings communicate in some way or another.

Without practising these methods in the beginning, realisation is as difficult as squeezing your existence through the proverbial eye of the needle.

As long as the self contraction, the self-sense, the ego, is sustained by the continued occupation of the illusion of a separate self-sense and its various projects, missions, directives, positions, viewpoints, conflicts, tensions, stories and vested interests then these practices are profoundly necessary.

Upon the dawning of the realisation of inseparability, the experiential and deep knowledge that no appearance, no thing, no arising phenomenon including our own existence has any continuous, separate, defined or permanent existence and is utterly empty of any 'self', only then a whole different story arises. And this is the beginning of Radikal Freedom.

We have looked at ethics as the foundation of practice, as a method of practice. We could also understand ethics as the culmination of practice.

When inseparability is deeply computed, realised and embodied in every moment then ethical behaviour, in other words love and wisdom in action, is all that can and does arise.

Without the guidelines of ethical practices such as the Yamas and Niyamas then practice simply becomes a practice of feeling good, just another way to adorn one's self-story with glittering jewels of fool's gold.

As the foundation of practice, pragmatic ethics define the movement of energy that the practice liberates. Pragmatic ethics creates the container for the inquiry that yoga is, such that this inquiry is guided towards the exploration and exposure of the self-story mechanism and then the liberation from its tenacious grip.

As a method of practice, pragmatic ethics are impossible demands that we can only fail at. It is in their failure that we have the opportunity to see reflected our self-story and its machinations.

We can see our craving, aversion and ignorant indifference clearly mirrored to us as we struggle with the demands of the framework of ethics. We see the manifestations of these three primary energies of the self-sense as delusion, fear, anger, hatred, jealousy, envy, greed, and untruth. We feel their subtle aspects dancing in us as withdrawal, anxiety, irritation, dislike, possessiveness, gossiping, white lies, feelings of blame and superiority, inattention, and simple unkindness.

Until we see these movements of energy in us and accept them as part of our conditioning, as the flow of unhelpful energy that we have inherited and co-created through our conditioning, then we can do little about it.

In seeing the truth of what we are working with we can begin. The disease has to be diagnosed before the cure can be chosen and applied.

As the goal of the ethical practices reach completion. When we know the truth of our existence as Brahman, or if you prefer Buddha-nature, then we can only behave in ways that spontaneously exhibit the reality of inseparability.

In most of the yogic tradition we can find frameworks of ethics that operate in the above manner.

First we will look more fully at the ethical codes in Patanjali's Yoga Sutras.

Next we will look into the Hatha Yoga Pradipika.

We will also take a glimpse at Buddhist and Christian ethics.

Then we will examine a more contemporary view on an ethical framework for practice and realisation.

The Yamas and Niyamas
The ethical framework from Patanjali's Yoga Sutras

If you now go and read through at least two different versions of the Yoga Sutras and focus on sutras 29-45 in chapter two, the Sadhana Pada, you will get a flavour of this ethical code.

Different translations and commentaries offer quite different interpretations, again from the fundamentalist, through the utilitarian to the libertarian. As you get more into such old texts you will start to develop your own way of making sense of these teachings as relevant for your life. Trust your heart judgement here and keep your mind and opinions open whilst developing your own critical capacities.

It is also worth taking a moment to read and reflect on the Kalama Sutta, based on the words of Shakyamuni Buddha.

Do not believe in what you have heard.
Do not believe in the traditions, because they have been handed down for many generations; do not believe in anything because it is rumoured of and spoken by many. Do not believe merely because of a written statement of some old sage is produced. Do not believe in conjectures. Do not believe in that as a truth to which you have become attached by habit.

Do not believe merely the authority of your teachers and elders. After observation and analysis, when it agrees with reason and is conducive to the good and gain of one and all, then accept it and live up to it.

And now, back to Patanjali who was deeply influenced by Buddhist thought. Remember The Yoga Sutras were composed around 700 years after Buddha's death. Patanjali grew up in an India which had been ruled by the great Buddhist Emperor Ashoka of the Mauryan dynasty which had fallen just 300 years earlier. So Buddhist thought still pervaded the India of his time.

Now we have a précis of the sutras on Yamas and Niyamas from Patanjali. These are not literal translations and many of the interpretations here have probing questions associated with them to promote and encourage both your enquiry and inquiry.

You have already had a look at other interpretations so you can start to find your own position with these teachings.

We want you to find your authority, to inhabit truth and we believe it is necessary to gently start this process from the beginning.

Sutra 2:29
Yama-niyama-asana-pranayama-pratyahara-dharana-dhyana-samadhyayo-ashtavangani

1.   Attitudes and vows leading to restraint of behaviour (Yamas).

2. Personal observances and principles of practice (Niyamas).

3. Being established and nobly enthroned (Asanas).

4. Understanding prana and its extension through breath regulation and retention (Pranayama).

5. The wise choice of interiorisation of the senses (Pratyahara).

6. Sense-of-self, focusing through the medium of mind and sense fields onto the apparently separate phenomena (Dharana).

7. Absorption of object as subject (Dhyana).

8. The wise-ecstasy of infinite view (Samadhi).

These are the eight limbs[1] (asht-angas).

Sutra 2:30

Tatra ahimsa-satya-asteya-brahmachary-aparigraha yamah

There are five kinds of Yama:

1. Ahimsa: (non-harming) bring no harm to the awakening of yourself or others.

2. Satya: (truthing) celebrate truthfulness and deepen in truth, be true to your word and let your word be true.

3. Asteya: (non-stealing) do not take what has not been freely given to you, no stealing of other's precious life energy, live with integrity and purpose.

4. Brahmacharya: (unicity with the divine principle)

find absolute connection with the supreme totality in all you do. Understand moderation as the path and over indulgence as an expensive distraction. Let all your sexual engagements be rooted in mutual truth, love, energetic synergy, deep awareness and complete integrity.

5. Aparigraha: (non-graspingness) find the freedom of non-fixation on any phenomena, experiences or promises of experiences.

In the next sutra we have the presentation of the 'Great Yogic Vow', realise as you commit to practice, this is what you are doing. Read it over and over until you start to feel its weight, its gravity and until it fully accords with where your heart is at.

Sutra 2:31

Jati-desha-kala samaya-anavachhinna-sarva bhauma maha-vritam

Together these methods constitute the great yogic vow, regardless of birth, family conditioning, origin, cultural conditioning, time or 'kalpa' in which one lives, duty or dharma and regardless of context. This is the foundation of practice and such a vow continues through lifetimes.

Sutra 2:32

Saucha-samtosa-tapah-svadhyaya-Ishvarapranidhanani niyamah

---

1. Please notice these are limbs not mere linear steps.

The personal observances and principles of practice (niyamas) comprise:

1.   Saucha: (cleanliness) this can be taken literally as keeping clean or can be extended to all realms and meaning the practice of remaining unsullied by distracted dualistic thoughts and feelings.
2.   Santosha: (contentment) the practice of appreciation of the natural perfection of everything as it is right now.
3.   Tapas: (heat) application of effort to extend to one's edges, whilst giving greed, lack, envy and jealousy none of the energy of your attentional fields.
4.   Svadhyaya: (self-study) consistent inquiry, using all available resources, into the deepest truth of existence. Traditionally this is chanting Om and studying the scriptures with the guidance of one's Guru.
5.   Ishvarapranidhana: (devotion to Ishvara) sublime devotion to the transcendent principle of reality.

Sutra 2:33
Vitarka-badhane prati-paksa-bhavanam

When disturbing thoughts and feelings threaten to disturb these observances, one should cultivate the polar opposite of loving and compassionate thoughts and feelings. This is an antidote, apply the medicine as needed.

Sutra 2:34

Vitarka himsadayah krita-karita anumodita lobha-krodha-moha-purvaka mridu-madhya-adhimatra duhkha-ajnana-anantaphala iti prati-paksha-bhavanam

Actions, including injuring others and harming their awakening process, whether performed by oneself, performed by ones agent, or even merely approved of, whether arising from greed, anger, envy, jealousy or infatuation, whether mild, moderate or intense, be aware they have unending fruition as karmic seeds.

Seeds such as these will lead inexorably to infinite misery and ignorance.

Avoid such a downward spiral through the attentional cultivation of the opposite. Realise inter-dependence and practice compassion.

Sutra 2:35

Ahimsa-pratisthyam tat-sanni-dhau vairatyagah

As you become established in Ahimsa, so enmity ceases in your presence.

Is non-harming (or non-violence as it is usually called) even possible?
How then are you going to practice non-harming?

Are you willing to see how any fundamentalist and literal interpretation of, and attachment to, non-harming could be harming?

Sutra 2:36

Satya-pratisthyam kriya-phalashrayatvam

Becoming established in Satya, being true to your word, your words resonate with truth and bear fruit.

Are we to practice aggressive truthfulness?

Is the truth easy?

Is the truth easy to discern?

Is there such a thing as truth?

Is there only relative truth?

What may be the difference between relative truth and any deeper truth?

To be an authentic practitioner we have to ask these questions, just believing in the dogma leads only to fundamentalism.

Sutra 2:37

Asteya-pratishthayam sarva-ratnopasthanam

Build a foundation in Asteya, mind and feeling focused in this integrity, all jewels simply present themselves.

Who gives what?

Who receives?

Who possesses anything anyway?

Sutra 2:38
Brahmacharya-pratisthyam virya-labhah

Brahmacharya is connection with the supreme totality in each moment in all you do.

Over indulgence and depletion of life energy through unloving sexuality is an expensive and foolish distraction.

When sexual engagements are fully rooted in mutual truth, love, energetic synergy, deep awareness and complete integrity, then continual remembrance of the transcendental reality becomes established even in these most potentially dualistically distracting of sensory experiences.

As a Yogin, practising in this loving way you will possess unimpeded vitality.

How will you continue the realisation of unicity in the intensity of passion?
What is your understanding of being one with the Divine totality?

Why might some sexual engagements be considered to reduce this possibility?

Is it that for some practitioners there are feelings of unloving-lust and objectification to work with that would in acting them out lead to feelings of separation?

What, if any, is the difference for male and female practitioners, in terms of energy creation and energy loss?

Men often experience ejaculation as an energetic depletion, hence its name in French as 'Le petit mort', the little death. Men also often experience orgasmic feeling and ejaculation as if it were the same thing.
Given it is possible to create orgasmic ecstasy in the male body without ejaculation and that this orgasmic ecstasy can be spread throughout the body and shared in deepening love with one's consort, and with the cosmos, is this a form of sexual continence?

Some argue that the lesser bliss of sexual ecstasy is of no comparison to the greater bliss of realisation. Others argue that the path of love is also a path to realisation.

When the two become one, is not the whole then known as holy?

Women are more than capable of creating repeated, blissful and ecstatic experiences either by themselves or in consort with a lover and to build this energy and again share it through breath practices, close proximity and through its altering the synaptic patterns of one's perceptual field.

Seeing from a place of bliss is different from viewing the

world from sadness, loss and misery.

What is the difference between lust and objectification leading to temporary gratification, and mutually loving, heart-opening sexuality?

Some people equate brahmacharya with non-ejaculation. Some people insist that brahmacharya means celibacy.

Why do you think this might this be?

Why is it that this single energy of life, sexuality, has been most feared and most controlled throughout human history?

There are ancient tales of sperm being the most condensed of the tissues in the body. Women were rarely mentioned or considered in older texts. Writing such as "place your left heel behind your testicles" is quite clear in this respect. Modern apologists for the masculist stance of older texts will nowadays state that women were meant to be included and will nowadays include female sexual responses and life juices in their medical frameworks.

Sperm, or as the apologists say, 'sexual fluids' are supposed to change from the most condensed physical juice into spiritual juice and power if it is withheld?

This sort of teaching you will find in both Vedic and Buddhist teachings.

In the Vedic culture they say retention builds Tejas and in Buddhism they say that it builds Bodhicitta.

What is your experience of this, if any?

Some more dogmatic and religious yogic traditions consider celibate, non-ejaculating men in dresses to be the peak life-form on the planet, many other patriarchal religions appear to feel the same.

Women in these traditions are often considered to be a lower birth, and in fact it is often said that it is impossible for women to be awakened or realised in any meaningful way. This sort of prejudice permeates much of 'traditional' Yogic thought.

What are your feelings on this?

Sutra 2:39
Aparigraha-sthairye janma-kathamta-sambodhah

When Aparigraha is established, the freedom of non-fixation on all phenomena or promises of experiences arises. Practising generosity, all knowledge of past and future lives is known.

For the true Jnani, for the one whose self-effort and realisation is unsurpassed there is no longer any uncontrollable destiny.

How far does this practice reach?
Does it not also imply no longer making any self-construct by grasping onto referential phenomena?

Self-references are the way we build our self-story, the I exists as a solid and meaningful entity because it has moment-by-moment proof of its existence. The proof of its existence is through all its identification points. I exist because I…

- Think these things

- Feel these things

- Do these things

- Have these things

- Am not this

- Like this

- Don't like this

- Am this

- Am becoming this

No longer fixating on any of these facets of the 'I' story whilst neither having aversion to them, Isn't this awakening?

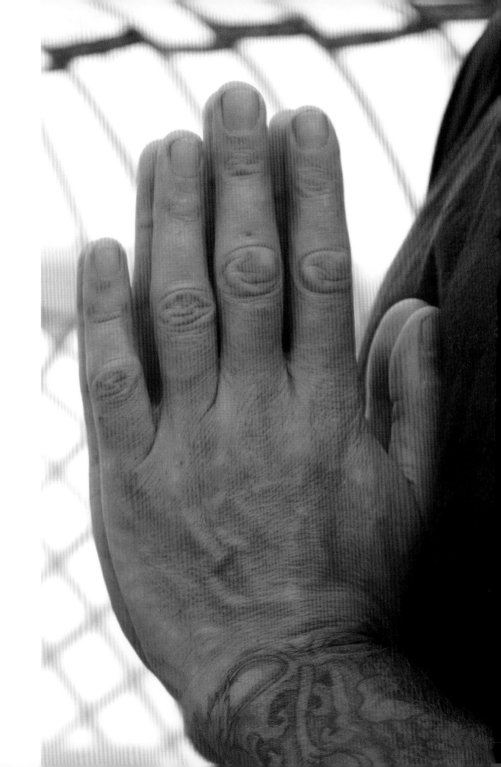

Sutra 2:40
Shauchat svanga-jugupsa parair asamsargah

When grounded in Saucha you will freely be able to remain uninvolved, no fixation in any realm will occur.

The practice of remaining unsullied by distracted dualistic thoughts, feelings and sensations means one's own and other's bodies are known as the flow of phenomena. Rest uncontaminated by samsara and see the beauty of impermanent phenomena in fundamentally new ways.

The more traditional interpretation of the Yoga Sutras tells us that Saucha leads to letting go of and even despising the body.

What does this practice mean for you?

Are you willing to despise your body?

Would despising the body feel a helpful strategy for awakening to truth and love?

Is cleanliness limited to the body?

What is your understanding of purity and impurity?

Or, is it that the only impure thing is the thought of impurity?

How can anything be impure if the divine principle is totality?

Are there ghettoes of the divine principle, less divine, where impurity lives?

Is the feeling of purity a relative position in space-time that is just another aspect of the illusion of separation?

Is the experience of impurity a mental fabrication crafting the 'other' out of phenomena and deepening the schism of feeling separate?

Sutra 2:41
Sattva-shuddhi saumanasya-ekagrya-indriya-jayatma-darshana-yogyatvani cha

Furthermore, mental purification, an inherent sense of joy, one-pointedness of mind, control of the senses and the readiness to achieve Self-realisation also arise from this practice.

Sutra 2:42
Samtosha danuttama sukha-labhah

Santosha, seeing all as grace, leads to unsurpassed joy.

Being utterly content, in acceptance and celebration of every arising phenomenon, unsurpassed joy is all that is then possible, isn't it?

Can you actually be successful at this?

What will failing at this practice teach you?

What will deepening feelings of non-contextual and unconditional joy indicate to you?

Sutra 2:43
Kaya-indriya-siddhir ashuddhi-ksayat tapasah

Through Tapas, which is the application of appropriately intense effort to extend to one's edges for the purposes of transformation, become free from greed, from lack, from envy and jealousy as your attentional fields learn to rest as empty-essence in engagement. Through this practice the body and sense organs are said to become perfected.

Empty-essence is free of purity and impurity, the freedom of the adamantine body arises and the six sense organs -
hearing, touch (including proprioception), sight, taste, smell and mind are liberated from dualistic distortion. This is for those who truly know Tapas.

Are you really willing to cultivate and apply continuous appropriate and diligent effort for transformation?

If Tapas can be more simply seen as meeting your edges daily and using the edge to grow, how will you be doing this?

With which personal developmental practices (sadhana) are you meeting your edges and giving yourself a stretch?

Or, are your practices complacent, resting you in a place of comfort, self-satisfaction and sedation?

Sutra 2:44
Svadhyaya ishtadevata-samprayogah

Svadhyaya can be understood as chanting Om, studying the yogic texts and scriptures and deepening in consistent inquiry using all available resources, into the deepest truth of existence.

Through svadhyaya the Yogin touches into greater awareness, wise-intelligence and union.
This wisdom applied throughout life establishes direct contact with the chosen Divine entity (ishta-devata) whose energy guides the Yogin to greater freedom.

What means do you have available to you to deepen your knowledge of truth?

How will you choose to more deeply inquire into both the nature and truth of existence?

What or who are you prepared not to learn from?

This last question is asked to help prompt deeper openness; life is your teacher surely?

Why might we shut down from him/her/it?

If you don't have an Ishta-devata, what symbols or representations of deeper truth and love might you use to guide you into awakening?

Is it possible to do this by yourself or do you need a Guru, a Lama, or a teacher as a 'dangerous friend'[2] to show you where your edges are?

Sutra 2:45
Samadhi-siddhir Ishvarapranidhanat

Ishwarapranidhana is the devotional surrender to the supreme Self, the totality of reality. From Ishwarapranidhana arises attainment of perfect supra-conscious ecstasy. Samadhi is attained through real devotion.

How do you practice devotion?

This is clearly an important and fundamental practice since it is in both in the Niyamas and Patanjali's Kriya Yoga.

By what methods will you expand your heart to open beyond conditional loving into the light of compassion?

Will you practice Guru Yoga?

This means you become a disciple to a realised spiritual

2. A term used in Vajrayana to describe the Lama student relationship, the Guru Shisya relationship in Vedic culture.

teacher and follow their every command with the aim of dissolving the self-story and awakening.

Will you practice as a Bhakta, a devotee of love?

   This probably means you will have a teacher, however if you don't how will you practice as a devotee of love?

Will you practice Bodhicitta?
Will you choose to see the essence of all beings as Buddhas to be and live this?

Will you offer your life in service like Mother Theresa?

   In some of Christopher's other books he talks about Bio-philia, the love of and devotion to life.

Is practising Bio-philia a valid path as a contemporary bhakta?

   In our view it is a profound contemporary practice that facilitates deep ecological and potentially integral realisation.

Will you continuously see your partner as the incarnation of truth and love?

Can you view her or him as your teacher and really mean it?

If you continue this sort of Tantric practice, will you view all of arising phenomena as your lover, your consort and be respectful, loving and in ecstatic unicity with all phenomena?

This is an authentic Tantric practice.

What other paths of devotion may be open to you?

Ethics from the Hatha Yoga Pradipika

The Hatha Yoga Pradipika is a great work by Yogi Swatmarana from around the year 1350 c.e. on the techniques and methods of Hatha Yoga.

It was probably a codification of an already extant lineage of practice going back several hundred years. This book lists the original founder of Hatha Yoga as Matsyendranath who is revered in both Buddhist and Vedic traditions as a MahaSiddha, a great adept. He lived around the 9th to 10th century c.e.

Hatha Yoga entered Tibet quite early around the 7th to 10th century and is related to the practices of Trul-khor, Tun-mo and Yantra Yoga as well as possibly influencing Ati-Yoga. Ati-Yoga was also influenced by the arrival in Tibet of Chinese practitioners who were practitioners of Chan. Chan itself came from Bodhidharma who took Indian Buddhist practice to China. The Shaolin schools arose out of this movement. Chan moving to Japan became Zen. Both words Chan and Zen derive from the Sanskrit word Dhyana meaning the stage of practice of absorption. We find the word Dhyana used often in Indian Yogic texts.

This work defines the following ethical guidelines. Notice both the similarities and differences with Patanjali's work.

Read a couple of versions of the Hatha Yoga Pradipika and particularly look at chapter 1, slokas 15 to 17 as these offer the pragmatic ethics.

If you read a more original version of the Hatha Yoga Pradipika you will also see which of these guidelines we have changed and perhaps understand why.

Which version sings out as most true to our contemporary context?

Is it appropriate to simply reproduce teachings from a context far removed in terms of culture, knowledge, understandings, time and place from that which we currently experience?

Is it wiser to critically appraise all teachings and take what is useful and then live by it?

Remember that yogic practice really is meant to be effective at resolving the illusion of separation and living in the play of radikal freedom. It is not enough merely to adhere to what may have been taught in a different culture 1500-2000 years ago. Doing this simply creates a museum of practice dissociated from any contextual relevance.

It's perhaps a bit like pretending dinosaur bones in a museum are giant living reptiles in massive forests and wide open grasslands with no real birds yet and only proto-mammals scurrying around underfoot.

Hatha Yoga Pradipika 1:15-17

15) Overeating, overexertion, over-talkativeness, dogmatic abiding by rules, excessive company of underdeveloped people, unsteady mind, these are the causes which inhibit yoga.

16a) Enthusiasm, perseverance, wise discrimination, reasonable experiential firm faith, courage, and avoiding too much company with those who are uninterested in the path of development are the factors which will accelerate success in yoga.

b)
Ahimsa - non-harming
Satya - truthing
Asteya - not taking what is not given
Brahmacarya - continence in continuous unicity with the divine principle
Forgiveness
Endurance
Compassion
Humility
Moderated diet
Cleanliness
These are the ten guidelines of conduct.

c)
Tapas - prioritised diligence in effort towards transformation
Santosha - contentment with all arising phenomena
Reasonable faith in the supreme principle
Generosity with all beings
Worship of that which is greater than one's small 'self'
Being fascinated by sacred texts and deeply studying these
Modesty
Having a powerful discerning intellect
The practice of Japa - repetition of sacred mantra with the breath

Appropriate sacrifice - giving up those experiences which at this point prevent or limit one's movement into realisation. Sacrifice means making sacred, returning to the one

These are the ten observances that assist development.

Before all other practices comes asana. Asana leads to steadiness and strength of body-mind, freedom from disease and a lightness and flexibility of the limbs (and the mind?). Notice that in this system Asana comes before the pragmatic ethics. In Patanjali's system the pragmatic ethics comes first. It is an interesting thing about Yoga in prisons how people practising funny shapes and sitting quietly can begin to desire ethical and love-filled lives. Either way one can see how the limbs of Yogic engagement begin to function together.

Designed to enhance congruence between the cultivation of inner attitudes and outer actions, these highly pragmatic ethical methods, these key demands, these ways of seeing the world are the preliminary foundations of a yogic practice.

Please consider these ethical rules carefully.

How do they fit in your life?

What do you think of them?

What interpretations and methods work best to facilitate ego transcendence?

Which translations simply ossify the ego and help build a lovely shiny 'spiritual ego'?

Do you feel these practices are necessary to begin a yogic practice?

Are they not also the culmination of practice?

What are your honest, ethical views?

How do they correlate with the espoused yogic views?

How do they serve your development and the greater good?

How do you know they serve the greater good?

Buddhist Ethics

In Buddhism we have three systems of ethical framework dependent on the involvement of the practitioner with the monastic codes.

The base level of pragmatic ethics are the five precepts, which are:

- Refrain from killing sentient beings

- Refrain from taking what is not given

- Refrain from sexual misconduct

- Refrain from lying

- Refrain from taking intoxicants

The more Tantric interpretation of these is in accord with what we have explored above. These you will find much more clearly outlined in The Song of the Owl Headed Dakini of the Aro-gTer lineage.

- *Refrain from killing the efflorescence of awakened nature as it sparkles through the fabric of duality*

- *Refrain from stealing opportunities for realisation*

- *To remain in ecstatic embrace with one's consort*

• Refrain from living and expressing the lie of dualism

• Refrain from the intoxication of duality and get drunk with primordial wisdom

The eightfold path is the basic outline of the Buddhist path.

• Clarity of intention

• Clarity of view, what is the goal of practice?

• Clarity of action, how do you behave in the world?

• Clarity of speech, do you speak truth appropriately?

• Clarity of livelihood, do you earn your living ethically?

• Clarity of effort: including effort to avoid false and unhealthy ideas and situations, effort to resolve harmful tendencies in oneself, effort to acquire necessary qualities and effort to maintain ones healthy notions and state

• Clarity of mindfulness: includes observation of body, feelings, sensation and thought, all internal phenomena and the workings of the mind

• Clarity of meditative practice: what is the appropriate method for your stage of development as a practitioner with your needs and strengths, do you practise regularly with diligence?

Christian Ethics

Most people consider the ten commandments to be the ethical code of Christianity.

It isn't, it is the ethical code of the Old Testament that went with a host of Levitical rules.

The pragmatic ethics of Christ's teaching amounted to only two codes.

When he was asked about the rules, he said: Practice these two and all others will automatically be being followed according to their essence.

• Love the Lord thy God with all thy heart and might and soul.

• Love thy neighbour as thyself

Beautiful and succinct, Christianity has often been short on what we call 'How To's' as is evidenced by it's witch burnings, relentless pogroms, inquisitions and other atrocities that completely misrepresent Christ's teachings.

This does not detract from the value of the original teachings, it means they are sadly open to interpretation and obviously difficult to apply.

Matrix Meditation

And now, meditate and deeply reflect on:

• *This beautifully complex web of interaction, inter-dependence and interdependent, co-evolutionary arising. Reflect on the endlessly interwoven cause and effect and begin to see your life in this new way. The realisation arising from such meditation is an important stage in development.*

• *Feeling, realising this profound sense of connection, now meditate on your body. Be aware of every part.*

• *Be aware of how it is a part of a much bigger whole.*

• *Be aware of it all as 'in flow'. Being aware of this form as flowing process resting in temporary cohesion before returning to the larger flow.*

• *Be aware of every complex web of relationship that has led to your existence and which continues to allow you to exist.*

• *Recognise and realise everything in your life as a continuously connected stream, one seamless flow.*

• *Now reflect on your emotional world and feel all the complex influences, positive and negative, that have helped form your emotional view of reality.*

• *See and feel your cognitive realm and recognise some of the*

vast input from the minds of so many Beings, past and present, that allow you to construct the ways you think, the meanings you make and the stories you tell about your self and your world.

• Explore this engaged, process-meditation in daily life. Reflect as you take food and drink. Reflect on systemic interdependence as you excrete. Be aware as you move, behave and relate in the world. Remember you are never not in relationship. During feeling and during thinking be aware of the vast complexity that allows you to be who you are. Relax into it, have fun with it!

•Arrive, in your own time, at a profoundly deep and joyful sense of gratitude for this life that flows through you and through all beings.

And Now…

Welcome and explore any practice that develops your mind and heart in a way that respects and honours this great and infinite web of connection.

Welcome and explore any practice that leads you into a deeper experiential realisation of inter-dependence and the ethical stances that support and live this realisation.

Developmental practices that focus on cultivating the capacities of concentration, power, will and manifestation can easily lead to mere ego gratification. Ego aggrandisement is devoid of this profound lived experience of an ethical and inter-dependent perspective.

There are many variations on ethical framework presented in the yoga traditions. Though the various codes of conduct and observance differ in some details they broadly cover the same ground.

Christ, as mentioned above was a developmental teacher of his time who brought the Judaic ethical guidelines down to just the two that he considered to be the completion of Judaic Law. This is our twist on those two profound laws.

• *Love all that is, as it is, (Divine sentience), with all your heart, all your might and all your soul.*

• *Secondly love your own Being-ness deeply and fully and then love all other beings equally as deeply until you recognise they are also the One as the many.*

These are pretty hardcore guidelines, challenging to master. They could be wonderful long-term goals though.

The next question that arises from such guidelines as these is how to implement them?

Contemporary Ethics

These twelve contemporary ethical guidelines are for the cultivation of awareness and kindness leading to Radikal Freedom.
These are the twelve spokes in the wheel of Radikal Freedom.

• These ethical guidelines are best understood as choices and practices.

• They are choices because we understand why we are doing them.

• They are practices because we recognise that we are engaging on a developmental process through seeking to implement them.

• Living these choices as practices makes life happier and richer for us and all other beings. It's that simple!

Awareness has the qualities of perceiving and knowing and has three basic aspects:

• The basic state of pure presence, out of which the dualistic mechanisms of self-construct and other-construct are fabricated through conditioned attention.

• Attention is a directional flow of awareness.

• Illumination or insight is the aspect of awareness that makes the unconscious conscious.

Kindness can be considered as heartfelt respect, appreciation and communicative care.

Try this commitment to Pragmatic Ethics

From now on, I choose to…

1. Cultivate awareness and kindness internally as much as possible and take personal responsibility for all my thoughts, feelings, projections, choices and the consequences of these in my inner life.

2. Cultivate as much awareness and kindness in my external behaviours as possible and be aware of the choices available to me. I take full responsibility for my actions and choices and the effects of these in my relationships and my life.

3. Study existence and knowledge of the inter-relatedness, inseparability and non-inherence of all things. I choose to act from this place of wisdom. I choose to continue to inquire into the nature of existence, with all the tools available to me.

4. Practice, explore and cultivate wonder, positivity, joy, contentment, playfulness, generosity, gratitude, love and freedom. I choose to find sublime contentment and wonder with every arising phenomenon.

5. Get comfortable with paradox.

6. Cultivate devotion to life essence and totality
and see the core truth of every being's existence
as pure, sparkling, naturally free essence.

7. Experience, know and communicate from
deep truth, beyond relative subjective truth.

8. Recognise if I behave in ways that hurt either others or
myself. I choose to learn as quickly as possible and aim not to
repeat the hurtful intentions, thoughts, speech or behaviours.

   • I remember there is no sin, no right and no wrong.

   • I remember there is simply unskilful thinking,
   speaking and behaving, or, there is skilful
   thinking, speaking and behaving.

   • I know that unskilful behaviour hurts others awakening
   and/or my self. I know that skilful behaviour helps
   others find joy and the roots of joy in awakening.

   • I know that skilful behaviour helps us find
   joy and the roots of joy in awakening and allows
   the planet and its myriad species to thrive.

   • I choose to cultivate skilfulness and lovingly
   forgive myself for past unskilful-ness.

9. Celebrate and honour the arising energy
of awakening in all beings and myself.

10. Drop guilt, shame and blame and other
unproductive, irresponsible and unskilful toxic states.

   • Adults seeking to control our life energies in unhealthy
   ways conditioned these toxic states into us as children.

   • Dropping these states I choose to free others and myself.

   • Guilt is temporarily helpful if it helps us to learn.

   • Shame is completely toxic.

   • Blame misunderstands the nature
   of reality and responsibility.

11. Breathe well and laugh often.

12. Celebrate creativity and make this life my art.

These are the twelve ethical choices and
practices for the cultivation of Radikal
Freedom

The Twelve Choices in Practice

These twelve choices when put into practice consistently work for the greatest and most evolutionary good. Using our minds, feelings, bodies and actions in ways that support this vision is extremely powerful. Even if at times we are unsure what this greatest good might look or feel like, we can sustain a powerful intention to enable this 'greater good' to become manifest knowing its essential elements of kindness and love, intelligence and wisdom, deep peace, presence and joy.

These choices put into practice constitute an endeavour to benefit all Beings in all the possible realms of existence. This is the advanced ego-desire of service, of giving, of contribution to the collective.

This vision of the 'greater good' activated through these choices, is the win-win-win ethical foundation from which all mind training and visioning can thrive. In win-win-win behaving, you win, others win and the whole planet wins. This is advanced eco-ethics.

Everything we create in our life begins in dreams and imagination, it then moves through the power of desire, is mediated by belief and manifested through motivation and appropriate creative action.

We can of course continue to create unconsciously and have no real developed skills in this area, in which case we simply recreate our unconscious patterns and shadows.

One could, however, choose to pay attention to possibilities of how to develop these skills. With the key developmental skills in place as detailed in The Book of Purpose, you could then easily move through the key awareness of unconscious-incompetence to conscious-incompetence.

Our wise choice from conscious-incompetence is always to develop any necessary skills and move through the practice of these skills towards conscious competence.

Real skilfulness is exhibited through unconscious-competence, by which time skills have become deeply applied and embedded in everyday life without our even necessarily thinking about them.

Of course we can also choose to continuously update our skills and become ever more proficient. Learning to learn and continuing to learn is profoundly skilful.

Dukkha, (dissatisfaction, discomfort or suffering) is in many ways our greatest teacher as it is often this difficulty that motivates us to practice, learn and seek change.

We desire, welcome and celebrate sukkha (ease and comfort), but the law of impermanence is always operational so sukkha soon enough passes, as all things do, and once again we experience dukkha arising.

Actually it is our dualistic attitude to experience, the difficult internal mental and emotional processes and habits that we consciously or unconsciously engage in that can make whatever we are experiencing into dukkha.

Difficult internal processes are most often triggered by an external context. We then use this contextual trigger to disturb and harm our peaceful equanimous mind and expansive heart.

We use the contextual trigger to re-inhabit the sticky old patterns (habits) of making difficulties out of 'what is' and deepen in our suffering. Is this skilful?

Unskilful processing is our enemy, not the external trigger. This difficult internal processing creates a dramatic illusion out of the experiences of our lives, an illusion we are ultimately and totally responsible for creating.

Suffering itself never awakens any being, otherwise all beings would be awake.

Only when we are willing to deeply explore, question and inquire, going beyond all belief, beyond all views of right and wrong and remove the cause and root of suffering, and resolve the belief and experience of the individual self, will we learn from it.

Change, growth and Radikal Freedom arises when we risk everything, cease taking anything personally, take total responsibility and, above all, cultivate a vast sense of humour.

From this base we can become involved with the exploration of all aspects of our life and start to let go of every psycho-emotional fabrication.

Anything less is less. So lets awaken, lets find authentic freedom.

If, every time we practice on the mat or sit in meditation we invoke the qualities of intelligence-wisdom and love-compassion-kindness as well as the recognition of the goal of practice, which is authentic freedom then we begin to direct the practices to transcend the self-contraction.

If every time we finish our mat practice or sitting in meditation we give up the energies and qualities arising through practice

*for the benefit of all beings everywhere then we begin the process
of directing the practice to transcend the self-contraction.*

And now we can start to take our practices into daily life.

WHAT IS ENGAGED YOGA?

So what is Engaged Yoga?

Engaged Yoga simply takes the realisations and insights arising from regular practice and weaves them into daily life.

Engaged Yoga is the feminine essence of yogic practice.

Masculine essence practice is cultivating witness consciousness and realising the emptiness of all phenomena.

Masculine practice detaches, it seeks stillness and the source of stillness, and it seeks the unchanging reality beyond any flow of phenomena.

In masculine essence practice, matter is just matter and matter doesn't matter that much.

Feminine essence practice at its best deeply computes this profoundly empty nature of reality and yet also recognises the flow of phenomena, the changing flow of reality, as not separate from this deep stillness.

Feminine essence practice is love in action; it is the flow.

Feminine essence practice is Engaged Yoga in that the flow of reality matters, matter really matters. In feminine essence practice, relationship and the quality of relationship really matter.

Remember that in masculine essence practice, matter is less relevant, of minimal interest and relationship is often viewed as a distraction to the search for freedom.

Engaged Yoga in its balanced form seeks complete freedom and love in all the realms of existence.

• Freedom, love and wellbeing as the realm of physicality

• Freedom, love, wellbeing and ease as the flow of energy and manifestation

• Core identity and freedom as emptiness, essence or source.

• Integration of core identity and phenomenal flow, recognising the two as one and the one as the two.

Engaged Yoga also seeks complete freedom in all the realms of existence for all beings and directly connects the search for 'spiritual' or yogic freedom to the work of incarnated freedom.

Engaged Yoga is authentic or Radikal Freedom in that it takes the wonderful intent…

"May all beings in all realms be happy and know the roots of happiness" …seriously and seeks this as a lived reality for all.

Like the Bodhisattva, the Engaged Yogin will accept no less than real happiness and Radikal Freedom for all, however it is that Beings choose to skilfully explore and express such a reality.

Skilfully simply means that the responsible and responsive exploration and expression of one's existence and happiness does not harm the movement into real awakening, happiness and freedom of other Beings.

In Engaged Yoga we work with the principle that it is each and every Beings birthright to have the opportunities, should they choose, to seek, find and live awakened and in authentic freedom and in response offer their full creative responsibility and potential back to the world.

Radikal Freedom is the term we have chosen to label the absolute freedom of core-identity beyond the identification with ego, beyond identification with the illusion of separation.

Some old school Yoga philosophies had Yogins dissociating, disengaging with the world, however from a more radikal non-dual perspective, this is not wise or actually even possible.

Knowing one 'Self' as Radikal Freedom changes the way one behaves and engages with the world. For sure a choice could be isolating oneself, however engagement with the world from the perspective of realised core identity is not really in question.

No matter what choice we actually make, from a realised and authentically non-dual perspective there is only engagement, its just a question of how we choose to do that.

As a contemporary Yogin we know that we are always in re-lationship, we know that we are also inter-dependence, we are relationship!

As a contemporary Yogin we know that we are always in communication, we are also communication happening.

The question that then arises is in what way will this relation-ship and this communication occur, not whether it will occur or not.

What are the most useful and conscious choices you can make around relationship, communication and engagement?

We already have some key understandings in place because as increasingly realised Beings the facets of pure-Beingness, com-passion, truth speaking or truthing, and bliss will be dominant.

The wisdom of knowing all flow as empty of inherent exist-ence and the native compassion for all aspects of flow that arises from this knowing of one's original nature, will effort-lessly occur.

We will not be settling for less than this surely?

The spontaneous play of pure-Beingness which now occurs in balance with the energies of wisdom and compassion allows us to facilitate others to know themselves and find the play of freedom. This play of freedom is not a static event, words such as truth, bliss, pure-Beingness and inseparability can present an image of some magical stasis, some still point that somehow is separated from everything else. For sure some spiritual seekers do seek such an outcome, just read the conclusions of the Ha-tha Yoga Pradipika and the Gheranda Samhita let alone count-less other tomes on 'spirituality'.

The way we are seeking to present the qualities of 'truthing', 'blissing', 'pure-Beingness' and even inseparability are not some static state of supposedly superior status but a responsive, spar-klingly spontaneous, scintillation that is the dialogue between the radiantly empty matrix and the flow of changing stuff, whilst recognising these two appearances are the unicity[3].

This dialogue is the awakened state, constantly awakened to this moment in all its ramifications, potentialities and possibilities.

3. Unicity implies that there never were two things, there is only inseparability! From the living experience of there being two things (ultimately as self and other) then the methods of yoga as joining together or unification are needed. The reality is that it is the illusion of separation that is dissolved not that unicity is created.

There have been times of confusion throughout history when reality was understood as split into matter and spirit, consciousness and form or some such polarity. The contemporary use of the word 'spiritual' almost instantly implies this futile and sterile dualism of 'spirit' and 'matter' as if there were opposite realms or poles of reality.

This unskilful medieval term is rarely used in this book, instead the terminology 'developmental', 'unfolding' and 'yogic liberation' as well as 'Radikal Freedom' are used as metaphors to represent the development of identity and perspective beyond that of the individual ego into the all-pervasive reality of boundlessness.

For sure some people use the word 'spirit' to describe this all pervasive inseparable nature of things, thats fine, but sadly most just collude and use it as a consensual term to avoid thinking about what they mean and present any act or experience as a 'spiritual' act, event or experience. Such 'spiritual' actions, events or experiences are most commonly used to adorn the spiritual ego, which is another very good reason to avoid the term.

Contemporary Beings aware of the exciting uncertainties of quantum reality might be aware of the current search in science for the great theory that will unite all phenomena, the Theory Of Everything. We love to call this the Big TOE!

Recognising inter-dependence, recognising the unity of all forces, all realms and universes in the great unicity, as sought mathematically in the big TOE, there is arguably minimal space left for such unhelpful dualistic terminology as spirit separate from matter.

Having said that, this sort of dualism can be a temporarily helpful method to move beyond addiction to aspects of matter. One can utilise the method of perceiving some things as spiritual and some things as less than spiritual to stop doing the things one has been addicted to. It's a method with some benefit, however surely addiction to limited concepts such as spirit and matter is itself unhelpful.

Non-dual Yogis have consistently pointed to the basis of all reality as radiance or clear-light (the big TOE?) Matter from this perspective is simply clear-radiance playing in the different vibratory experiences of energy and matter. Matter is simply energy vortexes that are simultaneously clear-radiance and the appearance of objects. Stuff is appearances as the form we understand, whilst also being energy flows, vortices and patterns and at the same time empty essence.

It can be helpful to translate the word 'spiritual' as inseparability and understand it as a metaphor for Integral realisation.

Integral realisation is the deep embodied knowing that all phenomena, everything that moves or appears to move, is in fact unified as clear-sentience beyond time and space, whilst flowing as the movement of energy and energy as form.

The matrix from which all energy arises and from which all movement as form arises is not separate from the energy or form. The play of energy and the movement of form are also this clear-sentience.

The slightly medieval and certainly dualistic metaphor of spirit separate and distinct from matter creates a viewpoint that could be understood as a product of the immature mind. The immature mind, aware that it can talk to itself and self-reflect, believes that the I-voice that feels meta (above and beyond) to its body is separate from its body.

There is certainly some fascinating research into near death experiences that seems to imply a separate 'soul' and body. The research by Dr. Peter Fenwick and Iain Stephenson's studies as well as the case of Shanti Devi on reincarnation certainly offer the idea that there is some continuity of some aspect of consciousness after death. Such research can be seen to support the dualistic view of spirit versus matter, yet it can also be understood quite usefully through the theory of yogic koshas[4].

Koshas can be helpfully viewed as the subjective experience of reality.

In what possible ways can and do we experience the world?

The yogic model of koshas is that our experience can be mapped in terms of increasingly subtle sheaths of possible awareness and sensitivity. The most gross of these subjective sheaths is the experience of the physical body. The next sheath is the bio-electric-magnetic field (BEMF), the experience of the energy body. The third sheath is the individual mental function of both 'I' thought and feeling. We can experience all these three sheaths and the next two as interconnected yet subtly different. We can also experience the sheaths as disconnected, creating a sense of duality. If we experience our physical body and yet are unaware, in any real way, of our electro-magnetic field, our energy body, yet also experience mind as resident in our head, it can feel like there are two separate parts, body and mind. In this way body and mind arise as the illusion of two, which we experience as a duality.

Yoga asana practice, yogic dance of awareness, tai chi and related movement practices as well as vipashyana meditation resolve this illusion by allowing us to deeply experience the subtler interconnection of physical body, electro-magnetic field and individual mind and then deeper into the quantum awareness field, the information field that is the universe.

Embryologically, we move through a stage where we are three layers of cells. These three layers are the ectoderm, the mesoderm and the endoderm. The ectoderm is destined to become the outer surfaces of skin and membranes. The mesoderm is destined to become the skeletal muscles and bones. The endoderm is destined to become the organs.

Yet something strange and beautiful happens. The outer layer folds right through the other layers in what is called an invagination and a long line of ectoderm then sits at the centre of all the other layers. This line of what was appearing to be destined as ectoderm becomes the neural tube. It bubbles up at one end to become the proto-brain and the line becomes the central neural line of the spinal cord. At this level of development we are still segmented just like worms. This central neural line then sends processes out from each of its segments through the other layers, these become the motor and sensory nerves.

The outside layer of skin, stroke it, stroke your skin now, is the outside of your brain. There is not a mind and a body, there is mind-body.

So if we leap directly from embryology to death we can peer into the Bardo Thodol, often called 'The Tibetan book of the Dead' and other yogic teachings. Such death teachings suggest that as we die, our sense of consciousness gradually withdraws from all the sheaths and their elementary associations of earth or solidity, water or fluid process, fire element and body heat, air and therefore breath and finally the element of space.

---

4. Kosha literally means sheath. The five sheaths are subjective experiences of being alive. The Taittiriya Upanishad describes them as 'the self of meat', 'the self of life-energy', 'the self of mind', 'the self of vast cosmic mind', and the 'self of bliss'.

Being capable of letting go of the associations and attachments of the self-sense and each of these koshas is at the heart of yogic practice. It is this capacity to rest in the elements without gripping that is at the heart of Yogic freedom. When we no longer solely identify with any elemental experience as the source of our identity or as a place of sanctuary then we are free within the flow of elements.

This is a very important aspect of authentic yogic practice. These subjective experiences of separate identity are then let go of and resolved as we flow effortlessly through the experience of yogic practice and then through death. When we can die without the fear that is commonly generated by gripping onto identification with the elements, we can also live in freedom, in courage. This courage is where the fear that drives us to create territory and create sanctuaries for our self-sense in the elements is finally resolved.

We may seek sanctuary in earth element through ownership and control (rather than stewardship) over land and property, in food and feelings of solidity.

We may seek sanctuary in the water element in neural system gratification and good feelings, through sex and through living in habituated and unconsciously reflexive patterns.

We may seek sanctuary in the fire element through relationships of power and control over others. This can manifest as submissive and dominance oriented relating personally or politically and belief in a big bad god, or necessity of another authority that punishes and rewards.

We may seek sanctuary in the air element either in loneliness and lostness or in the desire to consistently prove our relationship with existence. Either we pull away from connection and intimacy or we are in constant need to prove to ourselves that unicity exists. We will do this with the intensity generated through new lovers, new experiences, battles and their resolution or more and more intense practices. We need constant newness, constant feelings of being on the edge and constant proof through intensity that actually we are connected.

We may seek sanctuary in the space element through states of confusion and obfuscation and alternatively through getting spaced out or high. Some 'spiritual' practice is seeking this sort of play from confusion to being spaced out or high.

When we finally get that everything is already in unicity, it always has been and always will be. When we stop chasing and seeking and actually find what is, we can relax. Our sense of consciousness then has the possibility of resolving into the clear-light; into the clear-sentience, the information field that is the source and ground of being, free of contracting vortices of fear rooted in some elemental identity. This, of course, we can also do in each moment.

The map of koshas and elemental aspects of existence are both unified and yet also subjectively sensed as separate. That is why we have these maps and practices, to enhance the shift in perspective from separation to unicity. The experience of separation when viewed from a clearer more microscopic gaze is always one of fractal boundaries that are themselves none other than the membranous unicity of inter-dependence.

*All facets of being are now experienced as inter-dependent
and empty of inherent, real existence or non-existence.
Trans-personal identification with the vastness of the possibilities
and potentials of being arises through endless moments of clarity.
Clarity is simply what is, when we stop fabricating duality.*

In these moments of clarity we arise as the vast awareness we always were. Moments of clarity flowing into continuity, is the result of authentic practice. These moments of clarity lead to the stream of clarity that is the realisation of our truth as vast spacious sky-like awareness.

Identity becomes the enormity of aware sentient cosmic being-ness beyond the obsessions and confines of ones individual nervous system or sense of individuated being.

Yogic liberation from this realised identity is also an evolutionary stance that is also intimately connected with the economic, ecological, socio-political and post-religious freedom of humanity.

Engaged Yoga is deeply interested in conscious evolution and the realisations of consciousness as the play of wisdom and love across all the realms of existence. In this way Engaged Yoga is also the yoga of daily life, the yoga of doing the laundry, changing the nappy, building the business and working in right livelihood.

Engaged Yoga is all about relationship. The devotional love of life (biophilia) in alignment and service to the playful, loving and conscious evolution of humanity, is the consistent theme in Engaged Yoga.

Engaged Yoga allows a framework of practice within which the yogic practitioner realises their transcendent identity be-

yond egoic separation and yet also deeply engages in the world for the greater benefit of all.

Freedom traditions have consistently evolved and adapted their practices to suit different peoples, places and times, fully responding to the context and needs of the human experience.

In many traditions it is understood that transpersonal development and freedom technologies can only really work if they are appropriate for the time, culture and context. Hence the genesis and evolution of a uniquely contemporary yoga, a yoga that utilises all the modern aspects of inquiry from psychotherapy and psychology to physiology and physics in correlation with relevant aspects of the ancient philosophies of interiorisation and newly revealed treasures of awareness found in contemporary teachings.

The work of contemporary Yogins is to cultivate clarity and to open as vast awareness, whilst also cultivating discriminating wisdom.

Discriminating wisdom allows us to sift the baby from the bathwater; to distinguish valid experiential aspects of pragmatic philosophy from superstition, story, hyperbole and religious accretions of unhelpful dogma.

Authentic yogic methods are always liberating, they always serve awakening, and otherwise they are just a museum of practices. Such a museum is a fascinating ethnography certainly, but devoid of any real awakening power. What may have been a yogic developmental practice in one culture at one particular point in time may no longer be deeply relevant in a different cultural or temporal context. Understanding this, we do not seek to import developmentally irrelevant practices from another time, space or culture even though they are exotic, look spiritual or just make us feel good (though there is nothing wrong with feeling good, but mere gratification is limited). We do not use practice to boost our self-reference as a special spiritual being. Such approaches certainly lead to a special shiny ego but they don't lead to awakening.

We do experience ourselves as contextual beings, as relational beings as developed out of and intimately a part of our contemporary cultural milieu and this has to be fully understood, honoured and worked with. Engaged Yoga works with this.

Great practitioners and teachers utilise whatever is around them and use it to serve greater freedom. The dinosaur of tradition rests, fossilised in the museum of orthodoxy.

The genius of the principles of Guru (the liberating and evolutionary force of awareness) evolves any and every tradition as necessary to serve the cause of freedom. This is utterly evident through study of the annals of soteriological[5] disciplines. The Dalai Lama also suggests that all practices, methods and systems are designed to facilitate human happiness and that human happiness comes before the method, system or practice.

5. Soteriology is the study of liberation

Engaged Yoga has three primary responsibilities

First

Engaged Yoga, in total accord with the principle of individual foremost and method second, recognises the two difficult nervous system experiences for any Being.

There is pain, which is a physical event, and suffering, which is a psycho-emotional event. Pain is inevitable; suffering is optional. Though, of course, when we are embedded in our own particular version of suffering it feels utterly compulsory, necessary even.

Freeing our-selves from psycho-emotional suffering is our first responsibility. Recognising that whilst others can guide us, we alone are responsible for doing the work. This is a crucial step in our development.

Second

Having achieved this freedom from suffering, then guiding others to free themselves from suffering is our next responsibility.

Third

Protecting, as far as is reasonably possible, all beings from unnecessary pain is the third responsibility of Engaged Yoga.

Here it is worth remembering that pain is part of life, it cannot be removed. But we can seek to minimise unnecessary pain.

At this point it is worth considering just how our own lifestyle choices might cause other beings to experience pain and suffering in their lives. One such example is the westernised agrochemical industrial production of animal products that imposes short brutal lifestyles of suffering and pain for many sentient beings.

How do we choose to respond to this issue when we begin to take responsibility to reduce unnecessary pain and suffering?

What choices are available and how do we create more choice?

Sri Aurobindo of Pondicherry, founder of Integral and Purna Yoga considered the 'verticalist'[6], ascendancy strategies of some schools of yoga with their dissociation from mundane life and their exclusive ascent of attention in search of divinity to be highly incomplete and problematic.

This old school ascendancy approach downgraded the material world of relativity and form and exclusively focused on the super-mundane absolute as the only reality. It also considered all other experience and perspectives as illusory and ultimately totally irrelevant.

This ascendancy-oriented approach tends to generate a lack of kindness to form and a disregard of the issues of impermanence. It can therefore be quite an unkind and unloving teaching.

Aurobindo, in contrast, created Purna Yoga (Complete Yoga). Purna Yoga was not seeking renunciation via ascension and retreat from form but encouraged integration with all that is.

---

6. The drive to go upwards to God and heaven.

Engaged Yoga takes wholeheartedly the Vedantic saying "All is Brahman". Remember Brahman we can translate as Inseparability. Vivekananda understood all Beings as equally part of the great totality of divinity. Adamantly anti-caste, for him everyone and everything is the meta-theistic reality, the great totality.

Sri Aurobindo taught the cultivation of ascent, beyond ego, to greater realisation of consciousness and truth. This yogic ascent was then equally matched by the consequent descent of trans-egoic super-consciousness and the evolution of humanity into divine life.

Through the presence-behaviour, that is the pure trans-egoic 'Being-Doing' of the practitioner, we seek to empower life and create authentic freedom here on earth. This is Engaged Yoga.

Aurobindo's yoga relied on the practitioner opening to the divine through personal aspiration, the essence of which was self-surrender. This self-surrender allowed grace to do its transformative work. Aurobindo's followers of self-surrender, called upon the nature of reality beyond their ego (as the divine mother), and focused their attention during their search for deeper identity on their heart-space.

The heart-space has been seen as the key gateway to trans-personal reality and real 'spiritual' identity (the post-rational divine) since ancient times as evidenced in the liberation traditions of yoga, Hinduism and in the endogenous traditions of Paganism, Christianity and Islam.

The endogenous aspects of religious tradition are often more connected to the energetic origins of the religion and usually work with heart-centred interiorisation. Exogenous book focused, blue-meme[7] or highly superstitious versions of religion that often pre-dominate once the founding energy has become more systematised. This process of ossification of such traditions usually takes a maximum of five hundred years, often much less!

Engaged Yoga is contemporary, whilst recognising that it is rooted in tradition; it is conscious evolutionary awakening. It is appropriate for our time and culture, today's here and now.

Engaged Yoga is integral as it encourages practitioners to develop awareness and find inner freedom for themselves, as well as to positively influence all the walks and ways of their life.

Engaged Yoga is evolutionary in that it seeks transformation of both the individual practitioner, their culture, and their world.

Engaged Yoga seeks for our individual, collective experiences and perspectives of this wonderful cosmos and world to become as wealthy, beautiful and loving as we can possibly co-create.

Engaged Yoga stewards and wisely shares the natural resources available to us, and does so with the intention of co-creating the experiences of real love, prosperity, abundance and wealth for all.

7. Memes are the movement of ideas through collective mind space. Blue meme (initially from the work of Clare Graves) Beck and Cowan's 'Spiral Dynamics' represents a level of development where there is only one way, one 'holy' way. It is the path of rules, roles to play and ultimately of dogmatic fundamentalism.

The Four Viewpoints

All the theories and philosophies that seek to explain and teach how to understand life, along with all the meanings that define ways of making sense of our individual and collective experience, can be categorised into one of four viewpoints.

The philosophical and theoretical perspectives that can be categorised into these four viewpoints are usually promoted as the sole view of truth by the philosophers, teachers and academics that uphold that particular viewpoint.

The view being offered here, however, is a meta-position that explains the relationship between these four viewpoints.

Firstly

Firstly, there are those who have sought to understand and explain life from the empirical reductionist perspective of matter and its constituent parts and properties.

This materialistic viewpoint rooted in scientific method (initially as a reaction to the gross excesses of the church) uses empirical testing with sound methodology and can be reproduced by others. Such method is fantastic for examining that which can be measured and sensed by humans and their scientific instruments, which extend these sensory capacities.

Sadly, empirical materialists have often denounced all other non-empirical theories and teachings as ungrounded superstition (which they may be!), or irrelevant for the purposes of inquiry.

Science sees itself as offering a greater understanding of the deeper workings of the universe through the methods of science, which in many ways it really does. Science also offers a means of controlling nature.

Science simply works with the principle that the theory which fits with the currently available evidence provides the most likely explanation. In this way, a good scientist has the grace to not know and generate even more questions. Sadly, many religious exegetes 'know everything' and have no capacity left for not knowing.

Currently, at the edge of our human scope to measure the quantum structure of the universe, empiricism has created questions arising from empirical speculation that cannot yet be answered by scientific methods. For example, the big 'theory of everything' being sought is just as dependent on intuition, imagination and belief as any non-empirical theory.

Secondly

Secondly, there are those who have sought to explain life purely from an understanding of political and economic relationships. They believe that our economic relationships and political contexts define us. A child or adult working in a sweatshop for survival needs is not in much of a position to inquire into the nature of reality through education, or to make decisions that powerfully and positively affect the quality of their life.

It is easy for the very wealthy to access information and resources. Indeed, wealthy individuals often take survival needs, education, clean drinking water, medicine, and a reasonably egalitarian political process for granted. A 'greed distorted' democracy is surely still better than a dictatorship or theocracy.

Some political-economic theorists denounce all other methods of viewing life as fundamentally flawed and unhelpful to real political, material and economic human freedom. The world of scientific exploration directed in the interests of an economic and political elite who operate from a separatist and materialistic perspective, sees the interior world of inquiry as irrelevant.

Thirdly

Thirdly, there are those who explain life purely from an understanding of our collective nature as social and relational beings. Such theorists consider that all of our views and perspectives are conditioned by our culture, and that any belief, identity and behaviour we manifest is a function of this conditioning.

From this view, they seek to promote the understanding of social context and inter-relationship as the only real way of viewing and understanding human interaction. From this view, human freedom arises from co-creating cultures that respect individual choice, whilst contributing to the collective good.

From this view, all scientific inquiry, all economic relations, and internal inquiry, are functions of elitist hegemony and are viewed as dependent aspects of our function as relational beings.

Fourthly

Fourthly, there are theorists and teachers who seek to explain life from a mind only perspective. From this viewpoint, everything is derived from the internal subjective perspective and the externalised projections of mind.

Our sensory input and neurology are all we know and the reality of the external world is, in essence, a fabrication constructed from conditioned mind, and there is no way to freedom other than through the deeper inner view that liberates us from all dualistic distortion.

From the more fundamental approach of this viewpoint there is no benefit to seeking relational, economic or empirical methodological truths unless they support this internal inquiry.

These Four Views

These four views of understanding and explaining life and freedom have seemed essentially irreconcilable until the advent of the contemporary yogic philosopher Ken Wilber.

A part of Ken Wilber's valuable contribution is the reconciliation of these four explanatory views. His Four Quadrants model deeply relates to and informs Engaged yogic practice.

To experience Integral Engaged Yoga, Yogins seek to cultivate developmental practices in all of these four quadrants.

Wilber initially outlined what he called the Spectrum of Consciousness. This model seamlessly unifies the developmental qualities of western psychology and eastern spiritual developmental practice and philosophy. Outlining the transcultural developmental stages that individuals pass through on their way to greater being he has pointed to the unity of yogic experience across cultures. Partly, this suggests deeper levels to human experience than those merely conditioned by culture.

Since then Wilber has also mapped the construction of human ego through time and cultural history in his work Up from Eden.

The egoic fear of death leads to a desperate search for immortality and omnipotence. Arguably, the key destructive force driving consumerist materialistic 'progression' and ecological destruction on this planet is this very facet of what it is to be human.

More recently Wilber has created Integral Psychology and Integral Spirituality and again as part of this we find the robust model of the four quadrants. This (four quadrants) model, along with its associated lines and levels of development, allows one to understand one's own experience of the world in all its complexity in an integrated and clear way.

Wilber describes his approach to the non-dual reality as AQAL meaning all quadrant-all level. The four quadrants model allows one to understand the variously offered philosophies, teachings and models offered by humanity in a way that respects all of their strengths and brings them into a united and balanced overview.

Lets have a quick look at the four quadrants model. For a more detailed understanding please read Wilber's A Brief History of Everything.

To begin with, envisage a circle divided into four by a cross, creating four quadrants.

• These four quadrants are aspects of our experience.

• They are ways of explaining and making meaning of the world.

• They also map how we can develop our perspective and awareness and become more fully engaged in all aspects of the world. They show us how to achieve this through cultivating practises that engage us in each of these quadrants.

These four quadrants are labelled according to internal or external criteria on the vertical division.

• *The left side facing you is your internal, subjective experience.*

• *The right side facing you is the objective*

experience of the outside world.

• *The upper quadrants are individually focused.*

• *The lower quadrants are collectively focused.*

The upper right quadrant is therefore individual and exterior and can be called 'Its'. It is the experiential understanding of the bits and pieces of life.

The upper left quadrant is individual and interior and is one's subjective, interior view on reality, it can be called 'I'.

The lower right quadrant is collective and exterior. It is the view of politics and economics, the view of the others, and can be called 'They'.

The lower left quadrant is collective and interior. It is our combined subjectivity, it is community and collectivity, it can be called 'We'.

Internal (Subjective)   **External** (Objective)

I   Its

                                   Individual

                                   Collective

We   They

This is a simple map of the four quadrants

These four spaces are labelled 'I', 'Its', 'We' and 'They'. These four titles fit with both the individual and the collective internal or external experiences and explanatory styles of the world.

The Keys to the Four Quadrants

The first key

The first key to this model is that the world explanatory styles mentioned above fit into one of these quadrants.

• Mind only falls into the 'I' quadrant;

• Empirical, materialist presentations fall into the 'Its' quadrant;

• Economic-political theorists fall into the 'They' quadrant;

• Social theorists fall into the 'We' quadrant.

The second key

The second key is that all these explanatory theoretical styles are valid, and that they are all talking about the human experience from these differing perspectives.

One example is food. From a subjective, internal perspective food is taste. There is the sensory experience of eating and the feelings of food in the body. There is also the emotional content of nourishment and how we personally relate to the means of production of our food. All this is a true and valid understanding of food.

From a materialistic perspective, food is composed of atoms and minerals and vitamins, it is glycaemic index and does not deny the taste, aesthetics and feelings of the food. Both the subjective and materialistic perspectives are valid.

From a political, economic perspective, perhaps we could consider the costs of food production?

Do the methods of production promote food for all or just for the elite few?

Are the food production methods organic or not, and does this make a difference?

What carbon footprints are created by importing food from far around the planet?

Is there a better way to produce and provide food for all?

All these questions are valid inquiries from this quadrant.

From a 'We' quadrant perspective, food is about what our (or other's) culture teaches is appropriate, or not, to eat, how to prepare it and why. This view involves all the collective decisions that people promote and share through time and space about their dietary and consumption preferences. All these perspectives are also valid, they do not deny the other quadrants.

From an all quadrant perspective some views may, however, be challenged.

Can one continue eating endangered species purely because a culture says it is good, particularly when this cultural view was put in place at a time when the species was not in danger?

Can the eating of foodstuff produced in an environment of cruelty be considered valid when viewed from an all quadrant perspective?

The all quadrant view has the potential of a broader, deeper view that is understood through wisdom, intelligence, love and kindness.

The third key

The third key is about developing and transforming into greater being-ness in a balanced, holistic and integral way through how we choose to balance our perspectives and practices.

If we just go internal, live in a cave, do upper left 'I' quadrant practices then we will need to catch up with development in other quadrants at a later stage.

To go on meditation retreats and yet also be actively engaged in the world is to sustain this all quadrant balanced approach.

Recognising that family, the market place, and our whole life also form aspects of our developmental practice is to sustain balance and integration. To deny any of the integral aspects of our own human experience, and they occur whether we actively engage with them or not, is to become imbalanced in terms of an Engaged Yoga practice.

We cannot, in a body negative way, ignore what we eat or how we look after our body. We therefore choose to develop practices that nourish our physical structure from the upper right 'Its' quadrant perspective. We do this by paying attention to appropriate nutrition, intelligent physical practice and understanding the empirical view.

We choose to pay attention to our relationships with family, friends, our community and environment. We choose to develop, support, nourish and co-create healthy attachments (yes that's right, healthy attachments) and community. In this way, we support and are supported in our developmental work as a relational being within an evolving community whose members are taking responsibility for their thoughts, feelings and actions. We actively create communities of 'realisers' who facilitate collective wellbeing, growth and conscious evolution. In this way we develop in the lower left 'We' quadrant.

We also offer our individual and collective energies and contributions to society and consciously co-create greater wealth, prosperity, political and economic development and freedom.

Ignoring the political and economic aspects of life is not a wise choice, we are all part of these too. Food, clean water and appropriate preventive and remedial healthcare and education for all needs time, money and human resource.

Pathological power-centric politicians, corporations and militarists making war in the name of progress is a real problem. Pathological greed-centric corporations and their executives focusing solely on their own profit and acquisition of wealth is also a real problem. This usually involves the cost of and compromises the freedom, well-being, ecology, and survival of the planet as a viable home for its myriad species (including humanity) is a real problem. Such destructive practices dissipate collective wealth whilst concentrating resource into the hands of a tiny power-focused elite.

Policies of peace, reason, tolerance, respect, understanding, co   d conscious human progression require clear and
        hrough policies. They also require political and
        inancial backing, constructive communica-
        k, and emotional connection to the principles
        th the necessary physical implementation,

attention to detail in balance with the big picture, and service for the greater good. As practitioners of Engaged Yoga, we choose to work and have as much influence as possible in this lower right quadrant.

The fourth key
The fourth key is gradually and good enough.

We can of course take time to focus on development in one quadrant with the recognition that the others don't go away, and with the realisation that each quadrant, when effectively engaged with, supports and nourishes the others. We can gradually seek to integrate and fully explore our potency and possibility in all these quadrants in a creative way that allows and supports our progression within all the developmental lines in all quadrants.

'Good enough' simply means we are not driven by the foolish view of perfectionism. All practices of method, all inquiry, and all action needs to be only good enough to be effective for the purpose at hand. The purpose here and now is Radikal Freedom.

Integral awareness and practice engages us in a balanced way to be both engaged and effective in the world. Yet it also lets us be 'not of it' in terms of no longer acting from unconscious egocentric gratification or collusion. Engaged Yoga becomes a deeply enriching developmental journey on every level.

When we recognise the validity of these four different viewpoints and integrate them into a broader understanding we can form a deeper understanding of the nature of things.

For example, each of us has our own experience and practice of meditation rooted in the teachings we have received. This first person view is from the upper left quadrant. If our practice is akin to nature mysticism, basic tantric practice or some kinds of shamanism then it may take us into the psychic realm of internal experience. If our practice is deity yoga, more advanced tantric practice or deep contemplative prayer it may take us into the subtle level of internal experience. If our practice is Vipassana, deep inquiry, cultivation of witness consciousness, etcetera, it may take us individually into the causal level of internal experience. If the practice we are working with is more akin to Dzogchen, Mahamudra or Zen it may well take us into non-dual realisation.

One's meditation teacher might recognise such stages in the development of our practice and this is then a second position to that first person view.

The four quadrants map is then 'meta' to both those positions, putting the whole view in an integral frame.

Equally, meditation practice could be viewed from an upper right perspective as neuro-synaptic transformation, self-directed neuro-plasticity or a play of neuro-transmitters and the progression of development through congruent brain wave patterning, effects on the left pre-frontal cortex, gamma synergy, and so on.

From a lower left viewpoint a personal practice can be viewed as taking one out of immediate collective engagement. Some people who might be inattentive to its obvious and empirically defined effects may decry it as foolish 'navel gazing'. It can also be seen as enabling the cultivation of a deeper perspective of inner connections that allows us to take more responsibility for our collective engagement. This deeper perspective then allows me to re-engage with community more fully as a responsible, relational Being, hopefully from a less ego obsessed and more developed, integrated perspective.

Of course, any internal experience within our meditative development is also informed by the culture of our conditioning and the culture we currently inhabit and co-create. If you experience a vision in meditation then it will probably take the form of the cultural influences that shaped your thinking and feeling processes. These cultures and communities are both informed and co-conditional with the political-economic structures which manifested through time to the present day.

These political-economic structures are also informed by the internal development of individuals who constitute them. The way that political-economic systems (composed of cultures and individuals) manufacture, market and consume sub-cultures is a function of their psycho-emotional-cognitive and transpersonal development, as we will explore later.

A lower right perspective on our personal practice from the recently post-feudal, dominant political-economic paradigm, of 'democratic' capitalist consumerism (blue-orange meme[8]) within which I find myself born and living (and which I also seek to change, co-creating more positive possibilities) may be seen as a waste of productive time with no real purpose or meaning, or as a potential product to be sold in the yoga market place, a simple example of 'spiritualised' consumer goods.

We are never not in relationship, never not part of culture and never not also part of the political-economic structures.

8. The blue meme has been mentioned before, the orange meme is a developmental level rooted in enlightened self-interest.. This is from Spiral Dynamics, the work of Beck and Cowan.

Development in yoga does not take us out of these relationships, it changes them and deepens them through transforming our perspectives. We can potentially move from self-centred concern to a more global, systemic and integral outlook. The inclusion and re-integration of these all-quadrant views originates from the insight and deep experiential knowledge that arises from our practice.

We are never not engaged in form, as form and through form, for form simply is emptiness and emptiness is form, as the great Heart Sutra reminds us.

Yogic practices also fit quite naturally into these quadrants. How the practices work together and support each other can be seen in the diagram below. How we can develop integrally and nourish our own and others existence, wellbeing, prosperity and wealth on this planet through these practices can also be seen from this integrated view.

The yoga of food (anna-yoga), explores the effects of appropriate nutrition and, along with Ayurvedic inquiry, fits well with the empirical inquiry of western science into the upper right quadrant.

The practices of yoga-asana from Hatha Yoga also rest well in this upper right quadrant whilst crossing into the upper left.

The inner journey that arises through yoga-asana and related practices such as pranayama spans the upper individual quadrants.

The consequent deeper movement through meditative Raja Yoga rests well in the upper left quadrant.

Jnana Yoga, the knowing of who and what we are, leading to the dissolution of the ego-illusion, and ultimately the illusion of being a separate being, assists our movement into the reaches of the upper left quadrant as well as informing the lower left quadrant.

The bio-philic, ecstatic wonder of an Engaged contemporary devotional, Bhakti Yoga leads to a deep appreciation and love of one's own existence. Worship of one's partner, love of friends, neighbours and potentially even those perceived as enemies also offers this resolution of the subject-object illusion-no-illusion. Engaged contemporary Bhakti Yoga spans the upper left and lower left quadrants.

Karma Yoga is the giving up of the fruits of action whilst acting and working for the collective, for the evolutionary potential of humanity and consciousness, for the deep ecological well being of all of life. Karma Yoga also assists ones individual realisation as we ask:

Who it is who acts?

Karma Yoga is a rich practice of both the lower collective quadrants and the upper left quadrant.

Radikal Freedom, with its weaving of the techniques of personal practice, personal realisation as 'fluid process', and radiance, leads to high awareness and presence-action (Being-Doing).

Partner practices of loving intimacy, conscious sexuality and awakened relationship teach the divinity of all. These practices celebrate and cultivate the interior individual and collective quadrants.

Our involvement in mutually supportive developmental

groups and communities (Kula) now form part of a rich and evolving network of Engaged groups. These groups, working in ecologically aware, evolutionary, humanistic and engaged 'all quadrant' practices, are a contemporary evolution of the Buddhist concept of Sangha and the Tantric Kula. These radically free communities are manifestations of lower left quadrant practices, practices that affect and ultimately transform the lower right and support the upper left quadrants.

Realisation of Buddha-Nature as radiant clear-light, the source and ground of being, is dependent on one's individual internal practices and inquiry. The consistently engaged practice of kindness, love and awareness, leading to the realised experience of unobstructed compassionate energy and cosmic intelligence, influences inquiry and presence-action in every quadrant. This central realisation along with the realisation of inter-dependence is the basis of engagement in all four quadrants.

The four quadrants model allows us the capacity to see how the development of different practices can work in harmony with each other to create balanced and evolutionary development for oneself and all Beings. Gratitude to Ken Wilber for his powerful insight and work that he has shared with the world.

Engaged Yoga encourages the balance of awareness.
It balances the two drives.

The Two Drives

What are the two drives?

The First Drive
Firstly there is what can feel like a vertical, ascendancy oriented drive to transcendence, leading to trans-egoic experiential
identification with radiance as formlessness or 'emptiness'.

The second drive
The second drive balances this with the downward and hori-
zontal flow of super-consciousness as experiential identification
with immanence, or radiance, as 'form'. This flow of evolutionary super-consciousness then flows out into every quadrant, into every aspect of an engaged, kind, wise, consciously
evolving and aware life.

In this way the radikal vision of evolutionary yogic consciousness, of super-consciousness, flowing through all aspects of life
in our world now, is more likely to become reality.

This flow of super-consciousness manifested through presence-action (being-doing) allows real prosperity, real wealth,
and real freedom for all, to become our lived reality. The rich
understanding of the balance of internal and external development, the balance of individual and collective practice and
development, allows us all to experience the transformational
fruits of practice with complete integrity.

The map on the next page has labels of yogic practices and
related behaviours. These practices are placed into one of each
of the quadrants.

Some practices overlap boundaries of quadrants because they
cross those boundaries. For example, pranayama and chi practices in the 'Its' quadrant also leads one into the inner world of
'I', unlike empirical inquiry or fitness practice that is less likely
to actively lead one across this boundary.

You might notice inter-dependence right near the middle of
all the four quadrants.

Why might this be?

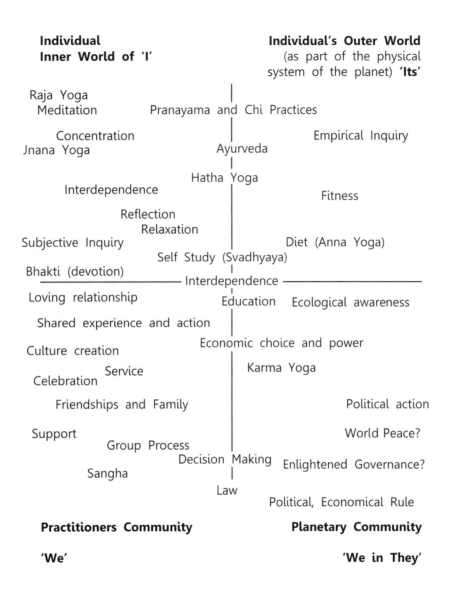

Mapping of Practices in the Four Quadrants

The Four Realisations

Any authentic yoga practice is going to yield insight and re-alisations about the nature of being alive and the nature of the cosmos.

Ultimately, if we look into any yoga tradition the unicity that yoga represents is a transcendence of the separate self-sense.

This transcendence opens us as beings into our original na-ture, which is the deeper matrix of awareness that underlies all experience, all insight, the self-sense, and self-story.

Yogic systems may present the path as being one of impersonal-ity, where the sentience or awareness field that is the cosmic matrix is vast and formless. Realisation of this vast formless sentience as our original nature is understood as wisdom, and results in unobstructed compassion.

Yogic systems may also present the path as being one of deeper engagement and dissolution into the personality of the divine. Whether this personality is understood metaphorically or literally, the process of surrender and devotion in itself ulti-mately leads to transcendence of the self-sense and self-story. The greater wisdom of the creative, organising and transform-ing energy that is the cosmos is then understood as one's deep-est essence.

The realisations that happen along this path usually include some variation of the following:

Impermanence

The deep recognition that this life experience is limited. This particular nervous system and its stories, beliefs and identity will terminate. Every living thing flows into disintegration, there is nothing that we can find in our individuated existence that is permanent, continuous or defined.

Inter-dependence

The fact that every single aspect of life is interconnected and interdependent to everything else. The reality is that there is no independence, there is only systemic flow. The contemporary science of ecology teaches systemic realisation.

Emptiness

When you take apart and utterly deconstruct every aspect of your existence, you will not find anything that exists that has any intrinsic or inherent solidity to it. Everything is flow, eve-rything is empty of any conceptual label of definition that you can possible apply. No constructs can define the deep nature of life as it is beyond such mental grasp. Some teachings call this formlessness.

The Non-dual

When emptiness is known and recognised as pregnant possi-bility and pure creativity then all of form is also seen as empti-ness. Emptiness is form and form is emptiness. There are not two things, there is only unicity or inseparability that appears as flow, separation, multiplicity and duality. This is integral realisation.

Again yoga teachings communicate this in a variety of ways, with differing emphasis, on what this realisation implies and how to access this one taste, or in Sanskrit *ekarasa*.

Living as yogic realisation

So, during the process of realising these four aspects of deeper yoga how might you live your life?

When any of these insights arise in your life, how might you be building a world in which these basic yogic truths are honoured and lived in accordance with?

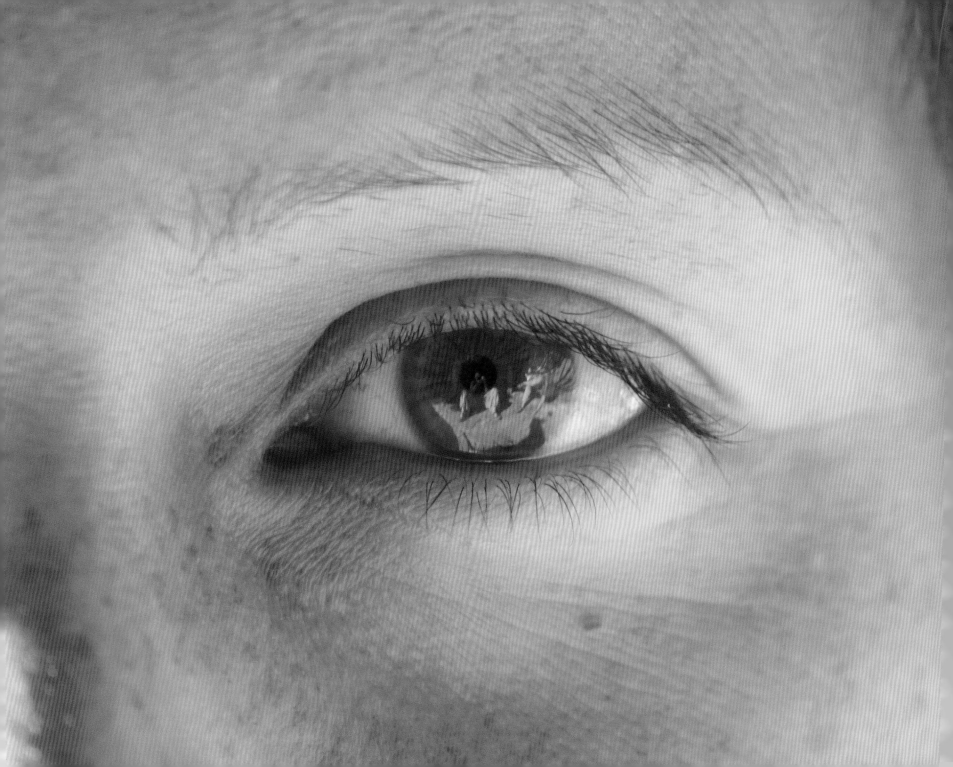

THE INNER EYE

Daily Life, the real practice...

We have looked at the rationale behind Engaged Yoga. We have looked at the history of practices of engagement and we have looked at the areas of life open to practice. We have also briefly touched into the scope of practices that encompass the four quadrants.

The intention of an Engaged Yoga practice is to spread realised super-consciousness throughout our life and into the world.

Lets take a look for a moment at Buddha. He was teaching in northern India more than two millennia ago. His teaching deeply touched a blood-thirsty robber called Angulimala. Angulimala wore a garland of thumbs, thumbs of the people he had murdered. Angulimala means 'garland of thumbs'. This brigand was transformed by the fearlessness of Buddha. Angulimala became a realized saint.

Ashoka was the emperor of the whole of north India, he was violent and warlike. Buddha's teachings touched his heart so deeply that he became a benevolent supporter of Buddhism and built universities, hospitals and schools. His life and empire were transformed through the ripples of Buddha's realisation. Buddha also influenced Patanjali, the author of the Yoga Sutras and Shankaracharya, whose teachings ripened into Jnana Yoga and were part of the creation of modern India and contemporary Yoga.

Tibet was warlike and violent before the advent of Buddhism there. The pre-Buddhist religion of this land was reputed to offer human sacrifice, and the Tibetans, as heirs of the Mongol warlord mentality, were powerful. Padmasambhava and his two consorts, Mandarava and the Tibetan princess and female Buddha Yeshe Tsogyel facilitated the transformation of Tibet into a land of yogic authority and non-violence. Tibet became the land of meditative realisation and presence through the positive influence and practice of Buddhism.

Do you believe in the power of your presence and practice?

Do you know the power of your presence and practice?

What evidence do you have?

If you wish for the benefit and realisation of all beings, do you fully mean this, or are they just empty (in the most vacuous sense of the term!) words that you utter?

Is it all just lovely platitudes or deeply held conviction?

If you practice 'truthing' then your words carry weight, they resonate with the authority of your realisation. In this case when you say such and such a thing you know that it is already happening, already in process.

As practitioners we are actively working with the power of mind, the power of belief, and we creatively and proactively channel this into the world. Don't we?

*So, we begin every practice on the mat or sitting in
meditation with an invocation to the qualities of wisdom
and intelligence as well as love, compassion or kindness.
We also acknowledge the goal of practice being authentic
freedom, love, and wisdom in action for all.
Now the practices can begin to transcend the self-contraction.*

*Every time we finish our mat practice or sitting in
meditation we dedicate the energies and qualities arising
through practice for the benefit of all beings everywhere.
This doesn't mean we just give up the energies, qualities and
merits of practice up randomly. They are offered up and
dedicated for the benefit of all beings. In this way the process
of directing the practice to transcend the self-contraction
continues whilst lifting the practice into everyday life.*

Micro-practices

• Micro-practices are moments of mindfulness and clarity in daily life.

• Micro-practices are opportunities for presence and engagement.

• Micro-practices are methods of carrying the depth and presence of formal practice into daily life.

• Micro-practices encourage moments of clarity leading to a stream of clarity.

• Micro-practices are a method of expanding love, weaving it through every flavour and nuance of daily life.

Two forms of stress and the self-sense

The sense-of-self and its relentless stories are commonly reinforced through the demands and stresses of daily life. Stress is largely a function of the sense-of-self. We can think of stress as two forms. These two forms do cross over though.

The first form is environmental stress, this includes temperature, sound, dehydration, starvation, poor air quality, and lack of sleep.

The second form is perceptual stress.

Perceptual stress is a function of the appearance of two. There has to be a subject in relationship to objects before stress can appear. This sense-of-self as subject then creates the perception of threat. It is the perception of threat that leads to stress.

Daily life offers a profound opportunity to notice not only how we fabricate our sense-of-self but also how we generate perceptions of threat and then build neuro-muscular stories of separation and stress.

Daily life offers the most profound opportunities to engage in moving beyond the narcissistic self-story into a real engagement with, and of, love and wisdom in action.

Yoga and yogic realisation really is measured by love and wisdom in action. It is in our behaviour that love is evidenced.

Micro-practices are a method of expanding love, weaving it through every flavour and nuance of daily life. Whether you are changing a baby's nappy, cooking a meal, sorting your accounts or shopping, every moment is available for deeper presence, deeper awareness, greater clarity, more love, and true engagement.

As presence and awareness become a normal part of everyday life, as clarity arises and begins to flow in streams of engaged presence, then the pouring of precious life-energy into the self-story diminishes and this fabrication slowly loses its power, loses its grip and becomes transparent.

Lets look at different areas of daily life and see how we could weave the practices of love-wisdom-freedom through them.

Sleep

We spend a third of our lives asleep. Recognising that sleep is also a place where sentience occurs allows us to begin to extend the practice of awareness into the realm of sleep.

Being sleep deprived, however, leads to arousal of the stress systems and can lead to all manner of dis-eases so we don't want to reduce the quality of rest when we sleep.

Through awakening beyond the self-contraction it is reported by many teachings and schools of practice that the needs for sleep reduce. If we identify fully with sentience rather than with the flows and changes of mind and feeling then it becomes less likely that we need to de-stress or regulate our neurology in the same way. There is little research into any of this at the moment though.

Sleep does appear to be either on or off to us. Brains can be both at the same time. Many creatures sleep uni-hemispherically, meaning they sleep on one side of their brain. Creatures such as dolphins, seals and birds have one hemisphere alert and one resting. This is probably an evolutionary strategy that facilitates survival. After all, when one is asleep one is highly vulnerable to becoming lunch.

Complex changes occur in the brain during sleep, as is evidenced by electro-encephalograms. After about ten minutes of resting in alpha brainwaves we go into a phase called non-rapid eye movement sleep (NREM).

NREM can be usefully divided into three stages.

1. NREM1... light sleep with irregular, shallow brainwaves.

2. NREM2... bursts of rhythmic brain activity, spindles and k- complexes.

3. NREM3... slow, deep 'delta' brainwaves.

Stage one is the lightest sleep, whilst stage three is considered to be deeper than the previous two stages.

After going through these NREM stages we go into rapid eye movement (REM) sleep.

The EEG during REM sleep is similar to that of drowsiness or even wakefulness. REM sleep is the stage where dreams most commonly occur.

A night's sleep usually consists of five or six of these cycles of NREM and REM sleep.

During sleep, there is usually also a reduction in heart rate of around ten beats per minute as well as a small fall in core temperature of around one to one and a half degrees centigrade. There is naturally a general reduction in both movement, motor and sensory activity of the nervous system. It is theorised that sleep offers us a means of saving energy, a method for regulating emotions, providing us with information processing periods, memory consolidation, and much more.

It may be that sleep allows for the regulation of autonomic activity such as heart rate and in fact sleep disorders are often associated with autonomic nervous system dysfunction such as a disordered heart rate.

Another theory is that sleep alters the firing of nerve cells and changes the connectivity between networks of our neural cells. It is theorised that this occurs through altering the timing and synchronisation of firing across these network connections.

The central biological clock that sets circadian rhythms in conjunction with light levels certainly affects sleep timing. Light affects cells in the retina of the eye, which synchronises the biological clock and affects other brain areas associated with alertness. Light suppresses production of the sleep producing hormone melatonin. The pressure to fall asleep when one has been very active is through the effects of a neuro-modulator called adenosine.

Working with computers, watching TV screens, and exposure to city lights and domestic lighting will all affect the quality of one's sleep. It is better to switch off as much as possible and be quiet for an hour or so before sleeping to allow quality sleep.

Sleep at night is of a much better quality than daytime sleep. Sleep periods are shorter in the day, the REM periods that increase as sleep progresses during the night-times decrease during daytime sleep. This means that we benefit less from the dream periods during daytime sleep and we usually feel less well rested. The sleep spindles in NREM sleep are also more abundant at night, these are implicated in memory consolidation so this occurs less in daytime sleep. Because of these and other changes, night shift workers stand higher risks of cardio-vascular diseases, diabetes and other conditions.

Sleep deprivation is found to be an aspect of many psychiatric conditions. One thought is that the amygdala, which regulates mood and anxiety levels and is involved in the perception of threat, is activated more in sleep-deprived people.

Deep sleep and REM sleep help with the management of the plasticity of neural networks. These effects from REM sleep could, therefore, help with the acquisition of new skills.

Studies of longevity find that those who live longest report sleeping between six and seven and a half hours per night. Women sleep longer than men and are also reported to enjoy a deeper quality of sleep. Women, on average, also live to an older age than men.

Practice relaxation before sleep and you will most probably rest deeper and your brain will more fully reap the benefits of sleep.

Remember that using computers, watching TV screens and sitting in bright artificial light before sleep will reduce the quality of rest and make it harder to sleep deeply.

A practice of reviewing and reflecting on your day mentally and resolving any unresolved issues before sleep is also a sound way of deepening your sleep experience. As the old adage says "Don't sleep on an argument".

Siestas are also a very good idea. Twenty to forty minutes of rest after lunch in the afternoon facilitates good digestion and allows for a level of rejuvenation that carries one through the afternoon and evening with ease. Many people seek to navigate the post-prandial energy drop by eating carbohydrates, sugar and drinking coffee.

Another useful strategy is to decide before going to sleep that you are going to rest well, when you are going to awaken and that you will wake refreshed and revitalised. Then you make it happen. Lastly, we can practice Yogic Trancework, Power Nidras and the preparations for Dream Yoga, which will be covered in the next few chapters.

Sleep well; awaken sweetly.

Dreaming and Dream Yoga

Dreaming is one of the states of consciousness which is rec-ognised in Yoga, and is a realm for Yogic practice. The other states of consciousness are the waking state, deep sleep state, and the transcendental state of consciousness which is the root and source of all the others.

Ken Wilber, who is one of our heroes, wrote the following pieces on the constancy of consciousness through all of these states in his book One Taste.

"This constant consciousness through all states - waking, dreaming, and sleeping - tends to occur after many years of meditating; in my case, about twenty-five years. The signs are very simple: you are conscious in the waking state, and then, as you fall asleep and start to dream, you still remain conscious of the dreaming"

"Then as you pass into deep, dreamless sleep, you still remain conscious, but now you are aware of nothing but vast pure emptiness, with no content whatsoever. But "aware of" is not quite right, since there is no duality here. It's more like, there is simply pure consciousness itself, without qualities or contents or subjects of objects, a vast pure emptiness that is not nothing but is still unqualifiable"

"Then as you come out of the deep sleep state, you see the mind and the dream state arise and take form. That is, out of causal emptiness there arises the subtle mind (dreams, images, symbols, concepts, visions, forms), and you witness this emer-gence. The dream state continues for a while, and then, as you begin to wake up, you can see the entire gross realm, the physi-cal realm - your body, the bed, the room, the physical universe, nature - arise directly out of the subtle mind state".

This is the constancy of consciousness through all three dimensions of consciousness, the final recognition being that all the states are one flow with transcendental consciousness. All of the possibilities of pure emptiness are utterly inseparable with the movement and play of form.

So, which part of our sleep cycle do dreams happen in?

Dreams occur in REM sleep and involve visual and halluci-natory elements. Such dreams will often use any and all of the senses.

But why do we dream?

Dreaming appears to function in a variety of ways. The first thing that is clear from scientific studies is that both REM and NREM sleep are crucial for mental wellbeing. The integrity of waking consciousness really does depend on the integrity of both sleep and dream consciousness, and getting enough sleep and dreaming sufficiently does appear to be crucial for human wellbeing.

Dreams can also highlight what we are not paying attention to. Dreams can bring to our awareness issues that we may do well to start looking at. One reason that people keep dream journals is that when issues are brought to mind (literally), one can then choose to engage with those issues during waking consciousness.

One may well choose to do this with the help of a competent teacher or therapist. If you choose to go for it alone, which is possible, then you need really good awareness and resolution skills, and probably some very good friends.

We also dream about what we spend most of our time thinking about and paying attention to.

What do you spend your time thinking about, paying attention to, and doing?

An established sitting practice will also help bring into view what sort of cerebral activity your brain gets up to. Remember, brains do cerebral activity, thats what they are partly for.

As long as you don't criminalise your thinking and drive it into the shadows or identify with it and believe it is who you are, that you are this cerebral process, or act mindlessly based on this, then there is no problem with any thought process.

We may well dream about recent memories that are emotionally charged, dreams really can help in emotional processing.

We may dream about any activity or event that is temporally recent to our sleep time. What were you doing just before bedtime?

You could also dream about any other historical memories that have not been effectively processed. The dreams here will bear some resemblance with the event.

Dreams also function to consolidate memories and to regulate and integrate emotions, particularly the more complex and difficult ones that we struggle with.

In this way, dreams can help facilitate emotional homeostasis.

Dreams help us integrate and make emotional sense of our life experience and its challenges.

Dreams can also act, as our thinking often does, as a form of pre-emptive threat rehearsal. How often do you have apprehensive thoughts about what may happen in the future? Well dreams also serve us in this area. We commonly do mental rehearsal of in our minds about potential social interactions we are worried about. Some solution focused therapies utilise this apprehensive capacity for performance perfection and generation of social ease. Dreams can help in a similar way.

Dreams also help rewire neurology, building new synaptic connections, in the light of experience. Our synaptic web is constantly undergoing changes in the light of experience, this is the very basis of neuroplasticity. Dreams, along with meditation, somatic practice, and a whole variety of therapeutic practices, offer the opportunity for rewiring the brain.

So, REM dreams are complex, visual and hallucinatory and their function appears to include all of the above.

REM sleep is also theorised to be prior to waking consciousness. This is evidenced by the occurrence of dreams in the foetus in the womb. Alan Hobson who came up with this theory suggests that REM sleep is also in the service of developing brain function, brain function that will eventually lead to waking consciousness.

Dreaming is a relatively recent evolutionary development requiring a link between the cortex and the thalamus in the brain. The cortex processes sensation, thought and meaning, and the thalamus works as an informational relay between sensation, motor function, memory, wakefulness and sleeping, amongst other things. This link is called the cortico-thalamic-cortico loop (CTC loop). No CTC loop equals no dreams.

Lucid dreams are simply dreams in which you are aware that you are dreaming. Lucid dreamers can cultivate varying levels of control over their dream states. This lucidity and control are probably achieved by switching on parts of the left pre-frontal cortex and another part of the brain, the precuneus, whilst keeping all other aspects of the body that relate to waking consciousness switched off.

Lucid dreamers score more highly on questions relating to self-confidence, tend to be more assertive, and show a greater sense of satisfaction, direction and clarity with their life. Lucid dreamers also report they are relatively free of mental health problems compared to non-lucid dreamers. Lucid dreamers may well process difficult emotions and trauma even more rapidly than non-lucid dreamers. Lucid dreamers have been shown to experience lower levels of stress than non-lucid dreamers in traumatic situations, such as war zones, due to their capacity to be in command of their minds processing more effectively.

Being in command of dreams may also open one to accelerated learning. People who perform tasks in their dreams have been evidenced to be better at performing the same tasks the next day. This is because the neural networks involved in both real and imagined tasks and movements are very similar. Training these areas through visualisation and Dream Yoga can facilitate enhanced performance in waking life.

Research supports the theory that neural networks involved in imagined tasks and lucid dreaming are the same. The benefit from lucid dreaming could be even greater than in visualisation practices because of the greater feeling of reality in lucid dreaming. This feeling is enhanced by the emotional content of lucid dreaming, which is usually less present in visualisation. Such lucid dreaming will boost the learning process.

Practising Dream Yoga is a profound way to deepen the practices of asana and meditation. Dream Yoga can be used as a method in conjunction with meditation. Dream Yoga can be used to enhance any skill, and yet can also be much deeper than this as it extends awareness through the dream dimension into deep sleep itself. To do this, a high level of witness consciousness is needed.

Dream Yoga, as opposed to Lucid dreaming, is much more about cultivating constant witnessing consciousness. It is carrying the meditative process into the dream dimension.

In Dream Yoga there is less desire to fly, have orgies, eat great food and so on. In both Dream Yoga and meditation the intention is to find that which underlies experience, not simply have more and more exotic experiences.

Dream Yoga allows one to apprehend the nature of subjective reality through the acceleration of interiorisation. When we also realise that dream reality is controllable, and similar to waking reality, we can begin to understand the role of awareness in waking, dreaming and potentially deep sleep and enlightened states of super-clarity.

Beginning Dream Yoga

Taking time during waking consciousness to study your palm is a good method to begin the practice of Dream Yoga. You need to study it well enough so you can call it up in your mind. Get to know its shape, its wrinkles, its idiosyncrasies and characteristics. Gaze at your palm, study it at random moments through the course of the day and get to know it well.

This simple method builds on the development of palm awareness.

The practice of lucid dreaming then follows these eight stages.

• Observe the palm of the hand before sleeping and decide to wake up in the dream.

• Now notice that you are dreaming.

• You will notice it, you will feel it because of the slightly unusual play of the senses or movement back and forth in time. The laws of physics may well be being transcended.

• When you first realise that you are dreaming then immediately raise your palm to your face and look at it.

• See your palm in the dream, when you hold it to your face you will know you are dreaming.

• Once you know you are dreaming you can begin to learn to control the dream.

• Through practice you learn to control the dream, resolve arising unconscious material, practice skills you want to learn and deepen in awareness.

• Wake up and remember your dream and integrate waking and dreaming consciousness.

Yogic Trancework

The practice of Yoga Nidra is a form of Yogic Trancework. Yoga Nidra means sleep of the yogin. Yoga Nidra is, at its best, a practice of deep relaxation, rejuvenation, awakening and realisation occurring in the realm between sleep and wakefulness, the liminal hypnogogic space.

There is a whole section later in this book on Yogic Trancework. We call it Yogic Trancework because this opens up the whole realm of liminal consciousness into a broader awareness of what is possible. Yogic history consistently reminds us of the relentless evolutionary tendency within the practice. So it is that contemporary yoga can absorb the best in positive psychology, solution focused practice, and other methods of hypno-therapeutic practice that also work in this delicious area between the realms of waking consciousness and deep sleep.

Yogic Trancework can deeply support the practice of Dream Yoga and, through this, the movement into awakening. Lucid dreaming has no necessary direction, it can be a fantastic playground for awareness. Dream Yoga, however, directs the time we spend lucid dreaming, potentially making it more meaningful, useful and integrated into daily life.

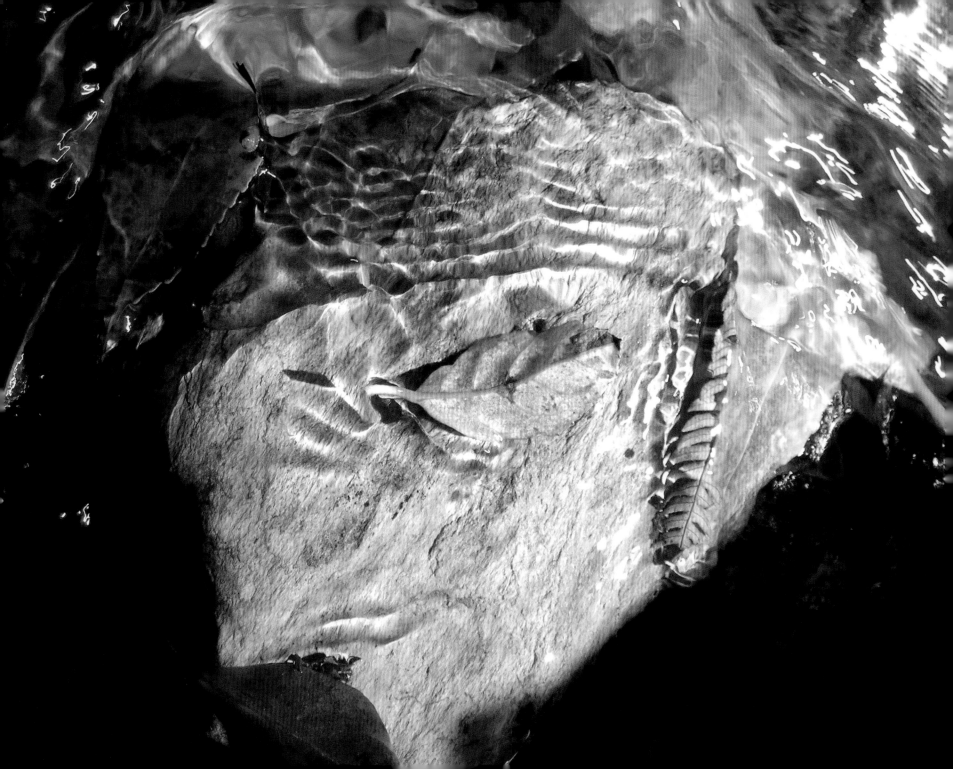

The Nine Steps of Dream Yoga

*This is the means to extend lucid dreaming
into the path of awakening.*

• *First, we have to realise that we are
dreaming, we have to become lucid.*

• *Next, to become steady and effortless in the presence of
awareness in the dream. Sustain lucidity with ease.*

• *The third step is to work with transforming
the dream and become skilful at this.*

• *Fourth, is to recognise all appearances as being empty of any
inherence. Here, we know that all flows of form have no solidity,
no definition of their own, no permanence, and are all products
and projections of mind. They are all, in essence, illusory.*

• *The fifth step is to come to stable, expansive, luminous
awareness. This is the practice of no control. Here we simply
witness, we observe all arising phenomena. We witness and
remain totally uninvolved, and deepen into this witness
state, this observing self, until it becomes effortless.*

• *Sixth, is to allow the witness, the observing self, to dissolve. The
dream flow can now unify with the clear light of awareness. this
unicity previously disguised by the witness, becomes self-evident.*

• *In the seventh step, we recognise in the dream state that
form and emptiness are inseparable, one flow. These seven
phases of practice also now flow into one another.*

• *Eighth, what can now arise is that luminous awareness
begins to osmotically leak into the deep sleep state and, as
mentioned in the Ken Wilber quote, deep sleep states also
become known as luminous awareness or luminous-clarity.*

• *The ninth and final step is understanding the essence
of deep sleep as luminosity, cognisant, aware and perfect.
This is then known as not different from one's awareness
in meditative equipoise, which one also practices in the
waking state. Dream Yoga is traditionally practiced
in conjunction with a meditation practice.*

Dream well.

Power Nidra

Power Nidra is, most simply, an enhanced siesta. It is a way of resting deeply within a state of rejuvenative relaxation.

Power Nidra is a method of remaining stress free and, in so doing, be more effective in whatever your chosen livelihood and lifestyle is.

Stress is the embodiment of the experience of separation.

Power Nidra is another method that can be utilised to keep you in a positive flow, and capable of responding with clarity to the arising needs and demands of life.

This practice has twenty delicious rejuvenating steps, enjoy them...

• *Sit in a chair or, even better, lie down.*

• *Now allow your mind to rest in the body. This is exactly the same process as in the practices of Trancework described in the next chapter.*

• *With Power Nidra you utilise the briefest periods of time to drop into deep relaxation, moving into source connection to revitalise and re-energise.*

• *Now, as rapidly as you can, drop your awareness through the layers of your muscles and bones, and then let them all go. Let them go with your mind, back into earth, returning to the element from which they arose.*

• *Drop your awareness through the layer of your organs and into the fluid feeling of pulsing blood, lymph and water, now let them all go. Let them go with your mind, back into the oceans.*

• *Drop your awareness into the heat of the body. Feel the fire produced from burning glucose in the cells. Recognise that all this glucose came through plants, originally from sunlight. Feel the fire and let it go, now let it all go. Let the fire go with your mind, back into the fires of the cosmos.*

• *Drop your awareness into the breath, feel your attention rest deep in the subtle nuances of the movement of the air in your body. Feel the gases permeate all your cells, one flow with the atmosphere around you. Feel the movement of the winds and now let them all go. Let them go with your mind, back into the vast open skies.*

• *Now rest your attention into the space within and between breaths, the space in between thoughts, the space between cells, the space between atoms, and the vast open space inside atoms. Feel the space your body is in, and the space that is your body. Now let it all go, be awareness, one with space, let it go with your mind. Gone, completely gone.*

• *Allow yourself to rest, cradled by the supporting universe. Dissolve into luminosity, as luminosity. Resting deeply as this, feel only peace as bliss and pure-being-ness, utterly vast, empty radiance.*

• *Rest as long as you need to here, in the timeless, space-less void.*

• *Gradually and creatively reformulate your 'self' and feel space in and around you. Allow space. Breathe space, be space.*

• *Move your attention into your neurology - the brain, the spinal cord, the nerves and synapses, the vibrant web of living sentience that you are. Be aware also of your patterns of thinking, believing, feeling and action, and find spaciousness, peace and stillness here. Allow sentience.*

• *Move your attention to the breath and feel the subtle ecstasy of the inhale and exhale. Feel the wind invigorate your existence bringing ease and grace. Allow wind.*

• *Bring your attention to the fires, the furnaces of life, in every cell celebrate joyfully the living sun of your body. Allow fire.*

• *Feel deeply the swelling waves of the ocean of this body as it pulses and flows. Let your mind dance in response to the powerful waves of life juices and their desires. Allow water.*

• *Let your mind settle deeply into the mountains of earth, crystal caverns and verdant fertile woods that are the organs, muscles and bones. Allow your mind to sing with gratitude and presence. Allow earth.*

• *With your next out breath begin moving these muscles, softly reclaiming their power and fluidity.*

• *Feeling fully incarnate, at ease, comfortable in existence, find endless energy and resource, creativity and vital living connection.*

• *Decide to fully awaken now, feeling energised, resourced, rejuvenated, revitalised and ready to continue your day.*

• *Take in a deep breath, then breathing slowly and richly out with the sound Aaaah, Awaken.*

• *Enjoy each arising moment of life.*

Yogic Trancework

• Trancework can be profoundly beneficial in catalysing growth and transformation. For many people their life is transformed into greater wellbeing by this practice.

• Trancework also has great healing potential as it reaches past both conscious and unconscious limitations of one's belief systems. Trancework allows you to access the resources of the 'other than conscious' mind.

• Trancework teaches us to access, rest in, and find comfort with these vast inner possibilities and creative resources of our 'other than conscious mind'.

• Trancework also facilitates the harmonisation of this newly found power and creativity within our conscious processing, enhancing our resource base and enhancing learning.

The names 'unconscious mind' or 'subconscious mind' are usually given to the aspects and structures of mind function that are either out of current awareness or totally unknown to the person moved and driven by this 'other than conscious mind'.

Unconscious literally means 'unknown', yet the associations with being unconscious, as in narcotised or anaesthetised, are neither constructive nor helpful.

Ironically, this most probably accurately reflects the levels of awareness that most people have of their personal 'other than conscious' psychological structures. Subconscious literally means 'under the known'. This is a good name in as much as it reflects the qualities of feeling underneath consciousness, and also that the conscious mind represents only the tip of the iceberg of our existence.

Interestingly, the traditional imagery of the second chakra is an ocean with a crescent moon above it, its animal representative is the great water reptile, the makara or crocodile. All these images reflect the oceanic and reflexive quality of the other than conscious, which the second chakra also represents.

Carl Jung introduced the concept of the 'collective unconscious' to the western world. This can be understood as a way that all minds interrelate below the level of the personal subconscious. Deep insight is a useful method for exploring the mind's potential, enabling the mind to be more fully known in all its complexity.

The continuum of personal subconscious and collective unconscious has been usefully named by the writer Natalie Goldberg as 'Wild-mind'.

• Wild-mind contains our pathological personal shadow and also the resources to bring this shadow to the light of consciousness.

• Wild-mind includes, beyond this shadow once resolution begins to occur, vast realms of undiscovered power, resource and creativity.

• Wild-mind allows us to make rapid, intuitive judgements.

Such judgements that can, potentially, make the difference between survival and death.

• Wild-mind allows us to access levels of awareness and deep potential that can transform traumatic memories and their resulting patterns of discomfort, suffering or trauma that can so easily debilitate our lives.

As traumatic memories are released we find the energy to move into greater potential. Patterning held in the part of the brain known as the amygdala, the part that remembers the essential components of trauma and initiates defensive action based on any experience that vaguely resembles that trauma, can be processed and released through Yogic Trancework. The limbic system that mediates our emotional experience can also be re-programmed to free us from unhelpful old emotional patterns. This allows us to move into greater freedom and find radically liberating energy where, formerly, one experienced anxious, fear ridden behaviour.

Wild-mind is accessed by resting into deep inner psychic space. Trancework facilitates this process beautifully.

As you deepen in awareness and mindfulness in your sitting practice you may access states of what we are going to call super-consciousness. Super-consciousness, also known as awakened-mind, is the trans-personal aspect of wild-mind.

Awakened-mind

Awakened-mind is potential, undiluted creativity, the source of wisdom, and one with the infinite possibilities of the universe and beyond. It is the information field and the root of all knowledge. Awakened-mind transcends and includes wild-mind. Awakened-mind is accessed through cessation of mental conceptualisation. This cessation is brought about through the practices of mind training and other appropriate methods of absorption, and the arising grace of insight and realisation.

The beauty of yogic method is that this vision of awakened mind doesn't even need to be true. It is not about dogma! When we act as if this were true, our experience of inseparability naturally arises. The experience of inseparability is now in accord with how things actually are, inseparable. We don't need to fabricate religious dogma, we just use the logic, deduction and direct experience of practice to lead us out of the experience of separate, nihilistic materialism.

The direct experience that is the potential result of practice, balanced with the wisdom of understanding inseparability, will also naturally lead us away from the New Age and religious states (often called 'heaven') of sparkling, eternalistic-monism towards real awakening.

Eternalistic-monism (EM) is where reality is viewed as 'One' without acknowledging the many. In this state everything has some important meaning, a crucial meaning for 'my' ego. From this EM view everything is meant to be, defined by destiny, and 'my' soul is on it's journey into the sparkling hereafter and phenomena are simply the signposts of the way to go.

If we inquire, "Who meant it to be?"

If the answer is a collection of dogmatic or superstitious beliefs rooted in either the fabrication of the devotee's mind, or an off-the-shelf belief system of one old religion or another, is that truth?

The egoic aspect of mind acts primarily through desire and fear. We may desire and feel growth, expansion and connection, whilst we also fear the loss of these feelings. We may also seek teachers and practices that offer us the possibility of learning these qualities and then grip onto the teachers, teachings and feelings as they become part of our spiritual identity. Now we fear the loss of these too.

Choice becomes the second gateway in the marriage between wild-mind and awakened mind as we start to, unrelentingly, choose strategies and experiences that deepen our experience of journey.

Having tasted a deeper sense of connection we become hungry for love, and through resolving shadow, following our joy and opening our hearts and minds, we can begin to experience a deeper truth.

Engaging in trancework is a choice to move from neurotic ego desires towards the more evolved egoic needs of growth, giving and service. These desires give rise to the unfolding into awakened-mind. This is concurrent with the gradual (or sometimes shockingly immediate!) dissolution of the power of the separate self-sense, or ego, to direct one's life.

In simplistic terms, the witness as a function of the ego looks down[9] into, identifies with, and experiences separation. From this view we feel the inherent tension and suffering of separateness. The witness, as a function of the ego, can however also choose to initiate the actualisation beyond itself (a task it cannot complete), and look into unicity.

Our experience then begins to transform and manifest as the un-grasped bliss of this moment, the here and now, the total presence and connection of nirvana, the awakened-mind.

These two facets of the diamond of unadulterated pure being-ness, wild-mind opening into awakened-mind, are the keys to unfolding into our experiential identity in the multi-ordinal vast awareness of our truth, which is pure being-ness. Pure being-ness manifests at this stage as the un-adulterated, resourceful Vijnanamayakosha.

Vijnanamayakosha is not about knowing someone else's thoughts, though these may be intuited. Vijnanamayakosha is beyond the process of what we would call thought. It is beyond mental construction and abstraction, beyond conceptualisation and might be more usefully described as 'deep intuition', 'bright feeling', 'gnostic presence', or some such.

One's actions are now spontaneously appropriate whilst living in presence.

9. I'm consciously using the verticality metaphor in this book. Since we are bipedal, we tend to move with the experience of evolution, development and luminosity as 'up'. We also tend to 'do' time with the future as being forward and the past backwards.
So, our psycho-spatial geography runs past back, future forward and development upwards, with regression or primitivism downwards in descent. What we have is ascension and descent, this is the verticality metaphor, that we mostly do unconsciously and believe it to be truth.

Wild-mind

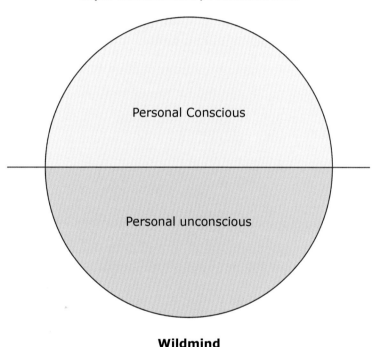

Vijnanamayakosha

Super-consciousness / Awakened mind

Personal Conscious

Personal unconscious

Wildmind

Trancework and Sitting Meditation

Trancework and Sitting Meditation are two different practices (amongst many) that allow us to develop the freedom to move into wild-mind and directly experience transpersonal, awakened-mind.

Both these functions of vijnanamayakosha can be accessed by other means. Artists do it, gardeners do it, runners do it, religious practitioners do it, children do it, so naturally as well as many other people and practitioners from all walks of life.

In essence, this direct experience is a natural human function, it is our original and beautiful nature, yet is often obscured by cultural conditioning and the ravages of growing up. We have most probably been told, and subsequently believed, that our basic goodness is childlike, and that our capacity to rest into trance is futile daydreaming.

Trancework can also serve as an evolution into new possibilities, new realms, that we choose to co-create. Through the naturally arising flower of creative inner discipline, and the practice growing from this, we cultivate the freedom to access and utilise these resourceful states. Without cultivating this freedom, such states merely arise as we engage in the activity that triggers their arising. Without creative discipline one rarely has any freedom or control over this process.

The primary difference between Trancework and sitting meditation is that in sitting meditation one is expanding in vibrant alertness as well as deepening into resting. Often in Trancework there is deep internal resting and the process work that goes with this, but not necessarily any concomitant expansion into greater alertness. There is great value to be found in the therapeutic process of Trancework, as we set our intentions and bring them into manifest reality. As part of this journey we can rewire our neurology to experience greater wellbeing, joy and happiness. Recovering the great treasures of creativity that sunk in the ocean of conditioning that we experienced whilst

growing up can at least be a fun part of our emotional archae-
ology.

How To…
The key to accessing wild-mind is through deep relaxation.

*Relaxing deeply is an art that requires one to be able to
rest fully and deeply in the body in this, and each and
every, moment. Such real relaxation is a rarity in our fast
paced, technological and externally focused world.*

The practice of Yogic Trancework and similar styles of relaxation all cultivate these skills and allow us to begin the journey
towards accessing our deep, inner resources. Many people con-
fuse activity with productivity, action with creativity, and running around chasing the latest fad or fashion with conscious
wealth creation. Understanding 'smart work', we work less, but
more effectively, for more. Believing in our value and our connection to what is, we can trust what is arising. Knowing our
capacity to contribute, we serve the collectivity of humanity.

Recognising the immense value of taking time to deeply rest
and relax, we cultivate the skills required to access some of the
most fundamental and pure resources available to us.

Please note, that if you are on any medication or have a history of mental health issues, it may be wise to consult a medical practitioner before beginning these practices.

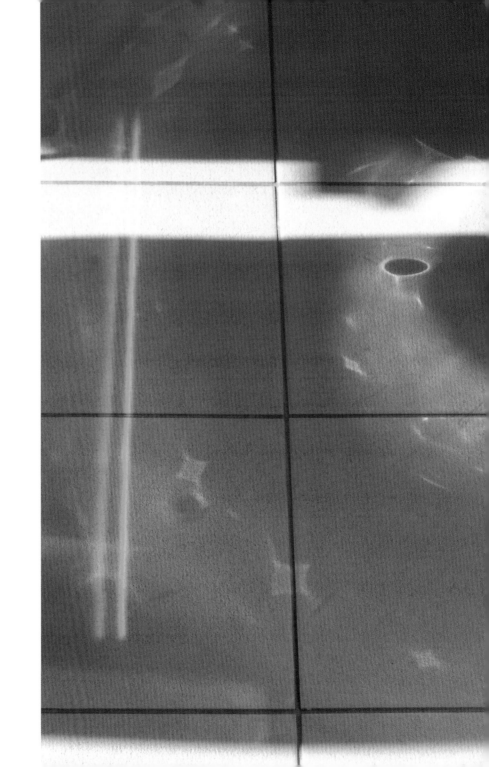

The Practice of Yogic Trancework

This practice consists of

• Three preparatory stages

• The nine waves of attention

Primary preparation

Prepare your environment well. Make sure it is warm enough, preferably with low enough lighting to allow you to easily relax. Cut out as much noise as possible and switch off any phones, and other intrusive electrical devices. Plan to give yourself thirty to fifty minutes of special time, just for you.

Consciously decide you will stay awake throughout this process and completely trust that, should any emergency or problem arise, you will instantly awaken, clear and conscious, ready to deal with the situation.

Trust and recognise that you will automatically achieve the best balance of conscious and wild-mind, so that all suggestions are readily accepted by the various parts of your being, and are effortlessly and beautifully acted upon.

Position

The second preparatory step is your body position. It is important that you are in a position that is comfortable for you, and which you can rest in for the duration of the practice, about forty-five minutes.

You can sit in a comfortable, yet supportive, easy chair with your feet resting firmly on the ground. You may choose to rest on the floor lying on your back, or perhaps on a comfortable rug.

If you have any neck condition that requires support place a folded blanket or pillow under your neck and head.

If your lower back aches place a bolster or cushion under your knees, thereby easing any pull on the lower back.

If you are in mid to advanced pregnancy either sit in a chair or lie on your left side. If you're lying down place your right hand near your face with the elbow bent, so the upper limb is supporting your upper body. Your right knee will also be bent at the knee, with the thigh more or less level with your pelvis.

Choose whichever position works best for you so that you can be really comfortable. Cover yourself with a blanket if you wish, and cover your eyes with a piece of soft fabric if this helps you deepen into greater rest.

Now fully and deeply rest here and find inner ease and comfort.

Intention

The third preparatory step of Yogic Trancework is to create a seed statement. This seed statement encapsulates whatever it is that you seek to co-create in your life. This is a wonderful opportunity to implant a suggestion for yourself that can really help you grow.

Remember, that when creating your seeds of intention they need to be worded positively and in the present tense.

Verbs in your intention should suggest your present action, not the ability to act or future action.

For example, instead of saying,

"I can heal" (ability to heal)

or "I will heal" (healing in the future),

one says, "Healing is happening"

or "I am healing"

or even "I am healing more and more fully with ease and gratitude"

All of these latter variations remind you that the action, in this case healing, is already existent in the here and now and will continue to deepen as the future unfolds.

Being specific is also important. Remember you will get what you are co-creating, so be specific! What exactly are you crafting?

Simple, clear language is often the most useful as it is easily remembered, incorporated and consolidated easily.

You can also 'sensualise' your intention to make it stronger, such as feeling yourself healing, seeing your success, or hearing your joyful wellbeing. This sensual content makes the seeds of intent even more potent and resonantly embedded in your neurology.

What will you see, what will you feel, what will you hear when the eventuality you are co-creating comes to pass?

These questions, when answered in the relaxation space, navigate your experience towards the outcomes of your seeds of intention. In this way you facilitate your own developmental journey, with ease.

Emotionalising, adding more joy and passion, again increases the seed's potency and helps anchor it even deeper into your body-mind structure. Feel all your cells joyfully vibrating with these positive possibilities. The more joy, delight and passion you weave into this seed of intention, the more you can really enjoy and appreciate yourself in this process.

Sculpting intent is an enjoyable art. As you practice more and more often you will see and feel these seeds growing into your life.

So keep it positive, keep it in the present tense, keep it active as well as seeing, feeling and hearing it happen. Remember, above all, be excited, passionate and joyful about these transformations.

Having created your seed statement as outlined, repeat this intention to yourself three times now. Feel it rest deep inside you, deep within all your cells, body and mind.

You will be repeating this seed of intent later in this yogic trancework practice. Repetition really works to accelerate and enhance this process.

Resting into the nine waves of attention

Feel deep into the body and allow the body and mind to rest.

The first wave of attention

Take your attention to your feet and heels and slowly move awareness up the body. Initially, pay particular attention to the contact between the body and the surface upon which one is resting. When you feel into it, the plane of contact is also the plane of separation, it simply depends on how you feel it. Whether the surface you rest on is the mat, the earth, the floor, a chair, or something else, feel the plane of contact-separation.

As you focus awareness throughout the body, feel yourself melting, softening within this contact.

The first wave of attention is to feel and explore this contact-separation.

The second wave of attention

Move attention through the body, starting at the feet again, and this time consciously experience each muscle group and each joint. Deeply resting within the structure of the body, feel the warmth in the muscles and experience a delicious melting feeling as you begin to relax even more deeply into the flesh and bones of your incarnate existence.

Finish this wave of attention with the head,

focusing in turn on the ears, the eyes, the root of the tongue, the lips, and lastly on the nostrils.

This second wave of attention explores and rests the mind in the flesh and bones.

The third wave of attention

Feel the whole body resting on the surface you are on. Feel the whole body, and now feel the breath entering and leaving. Entering and leaving, feel the breath through the nostrils as the whole body rests, the whole body resting more and more deeply.

This third wave of attention focuses on the whole body resting, and on the breath moving in and out.

The fourth wave of attention

Focus softly on each limb, feel the whole limb totally, feel it resting. Start with your legs first, followed by the arms and hands, then the trunk of the body, and lastly the whole head. Once again, feel the whole body resting, resting more and more deeply, and the breath moving in and out.

This fourth wave of attention focuses on the limbs and the breath.

The fifth wave of attention

Feel into each organ system, sending love and joy to each, and letting them rest in gratitude and appreciation for the awesome work they do.

You can omit this wave of attention if you wish. You could also try it another time when you understand your physiology more fully. You can also imagine where the organs are if you are unsure. You could also research them to deepen your awareness. Either way, if you choose to engage with this wave of attention, feel and totally appreciate each system.

Feel your fascia, and inside this feel the whole of the muscular system and the skeleton. Feel your stomach and intestines, kidneys and bladder, liver and spleen. Feel the lungs as the breath enters and leaves. Feel your genitals and reproductive system and celebrate them.

Now feel the endocrine glands along the core axis of the body, including your testes or ovaries, the adrenals, the pancreas, the thymus in the chest, the thyroids in the throat, and the pituitary and hypothalamus in the middle of the head. Feel all of these glands relaxing under the gaze of love and appreciation.

Release the nervous system, the whole brain, and the vast network of nerves flowing to and from every part of your body. Allow your body to rest deeply as you sustain relaxed function and attention. Feel the heart pumping and the blood moving through the circulatory system, let it all rest in effortless being.

Feel the whole body rest more and more deeply. The whole body resting, all the organ systems resting, whilst the breath flows.

This fifth wave of attention focuses on the organs and the breath.

The sixth wave of attention

Rest your mind's attention now more fully on the movement of the breath. Feel the breath move in and out of the body through the nostrils. Spend a few moments here resting in this breath awareness and become this ocean of breath, flowing in and flowing out. As you experience this you will naturally find yourself relaxing even more deeply.

Now deepen your attention and begin to feel the breath's movement little by little. Feel the ribs expanding, feel the belly moving, and feel the responsive dance of the pelvic floor. How much of the subtle nuances of each breath can you feel? As you rest into the breath so completely, it may feel like you are simply the ocean of breath and that this breath moves you.

Deeply soften your attention now and begin to count your breaths. Count from 21 down towards zero. If you lose count it doesn't matter, you can go back to the beginning and start again. Many people rarely reach past four. There is no problem with arriving at any particular number, just enjoy this practice wherever it goes.

Some people find this a useful way to rest still deeper into this gentle trance space. Some just go so deep whilst sustaining clarity of awareness that this is not helpful. What works best for you?

This sixth wave of attention is focusing on the qualities of the breath.

The seventh wave of attention

Either way, you will find yourself dropping deeper into this light trance state, this relaxation space, more and more fully. How deep can you allow yourself to go, you may wonder? You can, of course, deepen the trance state simply by choosing to. You can facilitate this by saying to yourself "I am counting myself deeper into this trance by counting down from 10 to 1. With every number I count I will float down 10% more deeply into this trance state".

When you have counted down to 1, you will find you have floated all the way down, deep into your own inner world. Some people, instead of going deeper by percentages, like to envisage themselves stepping down wide, beautiful stone steps. Step down one luxurious step at a time with each number, from 10 down to 1, until you reach the bottom, all the way down, and step off deep into your inner world.

This seventh wave of attention is simply deepening into the creative space of Yogic Trancework.

The eighth wave of attention

However you have chosen to access and deepen this trance space you will now find yourself deep down in your inner world. What is your favourite and chosen way of representing this deep inner space?

Some people create an exquisitely beautiful garden.

Some folk create a special room that they alone have a golden key for, with which they pass through the magical door into their sacred and special space.

Some like to find themselves on a tropical beach under a clear blue sky.

Yet others find themselves in another form of personal inner paradise.

Whatever works best for you, on this occasion, is just what you need. Trust wild-mind to give you exactly what you most deeply need. In this realm of inner space you can also engage in any practices you want to, such as your yoga asana or meditation. You can also address and heal old wounds of the physical, emotional, mental and bliss bodies.

In this space you can also find new creativity and possibilities around any corner, and of course you can plant the 'seed of your intent', which you remember from the beginning of the practice. It is useful to repeat this 'seed of intent' to yourself three or four times here. You might envisage yourself planting a beautiful seed in the soil of your inner garden. Wherever you plant your seed, watch it sprout and begin to grow into a thriving plant in no time. Watch it unfurl in front of your eyes, vibrant, magic and powerful.

In this deep inner world of unlimited possibility you can also vision your future, co-creating it in the most beautiful way possible for yourself. In your inner world there is no time, no space, and no reality, unless you co-create it.

You can do anything you want and then use this as a foundation to begin manifesting in your outer world.

Remember that everything moves through imagination and desire, through belief and values, through thought, speech, action and relationship, into manifest reality. It is here that we can find a fertile space to take deep counsel with all the parts of our Being.

It is here we can find answers to our most demanding questions, and step into the journey of finding the rich seam, the inner goldmine of creative resource.

This eighth wave of attention is to explore and utilise the wondrous resource of our inner world, enabling us to manifest positive change and growth in our outer world.

The ninth wave of attention

'Coming up'
When you have completed your mission for today, you prepare to say goodbye to your inner realm and to start counting up and out of your trance space. If you descended down steps walk to the bottom of those same steps again now. If you floated down with percentages, then find yourself in the same place you arrived at in your inner world.

Before you begin to count back up you remind yourself that everything you have set in motion (or something even better!) will come to pass. Also, know that you will wake up feeling deeply rested, fully rejuvenated and

resourced, refreshed, and ready to continue your day.

Now remind yourself that you will wake up more and more fully on each number from 1 to 10. At number 8 you will open your eyes and at number 10 you will be fully wide awake with all senses back to normal, alert, refreshed and ready for whatever follows.

Then, either as you climb those steps or float fully back into your body, count as follows -

"Number one, waking up, waking up,
two, waking up waking up,
three, waking up waking up"
etcetera, until you reach number eight, when you add
"Eyes wide open", and then at number ten you say
"Ten, wide awake, alert and aware".

If you feel drowsy at all, then please repeat this counting sequence.

The ninth wave of attention is coming up from the trance space, coming back to full external awareness.

Be Excited

Be clear, be excited, because every thing you manifest moves from this deep, magical space. Now let go to the fullness of the 'multiverse', of which your inner realm is also an inseparable part.

These Nine waves of attention are:
• Plane of contact

• Flesh and bones

• Whole body and the breath

• Limbs and the breath

• Organs and the breath

• Qualities of the breath

• Deepening into the creative space

• Utilise the wondrous resource of inner creativity

• Coming up

The Freedom of Zero-Trance

Many people live perpetually entranced by their habitual negative mind states and thinking patterns, wandering aimlessly and endlessly in cycles of trance, through their unconsciously chosen pathways of thought and feeling, in an endless parade of unconscious attention.

The whole time, these thought and feeling patterns continue consuming life energy and frittering away the powers of intention in fruitless mental chatter and feelings of fear and comparison. Fear is the dance of un-love, and comparison is the thief of joy.

Many people also live with trancelike addictions to food,

various narcotics, abusive relationships, and negative feelings, which are the bio-chemical states of one's own (unconscious) choosing.

Every one of these dynamics has a trance-like, self-medicating quality that numbs and anaesthetises reality, whilst consuming possibility and annihilating freedom. Continuing to create and recreate such negative, neurological default patterns sustains a lower level of existence than one's potential would otherwise allow.

Ultimately in trancework we seek to shine the light of awareness deeper into wild-mind whilst respecting its eternal mystery. Cultivating a healthy and trusting relationship with the less conscious aspects of wild-mind is part of learning to recognise our deeper nature as enlightened process.

This opening into spontaneously arising natural awareness of existence as radiance and rich possibility doesn't happen by imagining light beings 'out there' somewhere, but by shining the light of awareness deeper into wild-mind. As a consequence of this work we, and our actions, resonate with awareness and shine with its light.

And so it is through all our progressive practices of creativity, practices of real wealth, we step more often into the no-trance state, the zero-trance state of full presence, being here and now, being awakened-mind.

Trancework is an en-trance to un-trance into zero-trance, or no-trance. This is just another way of saying 'unfolding into awakened mind'.

Repetition is nourishing food for practice. Repetition allows the seeds of change to thrive extremely well, so please repeat this process often. Simply decide to deepen into trance-no-trance with greater ease each and every time.

You could practice this before getting out of bed in the morning. You could practice before falling asleep. You could practice at lunchtime. Just don't practice whilst driving or operating heavy machinery!

When proficient, this practice takes between twenty and forty-five minutes.

Waking Up

Waking up in the morning is an opportunity to cultivate gratitude.

Gratitude is the only real prayer of devotion as it is a celebration of whatever is arising. Rumi called depression 'the inability to give thanks'. Whilst this may be a limited view of that complex condition, it certainly offers an interesting perspective on our oft seen inability to be in gratitude for all that is wonderful in our lives.

The cultivation of gratitude is a profoundly liberating practice that allows more acceptance of life's agonies and ecstasies without us running from either.

Waking up is an opportunity, when the mind is quiet before the day's activities commence, to sit in deep contemplation, to make love with our beloved partner, or to cuddle up with the children.

> *Love, in all its forms, is an act of worship. Accepting the blessings of life is also an act of worship.*

Waking up in the morning is an opportunity to start again, to prepare your mind and heart for the day ahead.

Ablutions

Water is a blessing. Clean drinking water is a profound gift. Many people across this planet have to travel miles to get clean water. Many don't get clean water. Contemporary people from the industrialised nations often take clean water so much for granted.

Do you take clean-enough water for granted?

Wash with love, wash with gratitude and appreciation for your incredible good fortune and seek to create such good fortune for all.

Washing is a symbolic act of purity. Purity, is of course, a n illusion from a position of relativity. What can possibly be impure when the whole universe is Divine?

Isn't the very idea of impurity the only act of impurity?

Yes, we could explore this dynamic of purity and impurity as the lives of many great Tantric masters attest. The self-contraction, when it is lived as a tight fitting identity, is the root of selfishness, anger, hatred, jealousy, blame and shame.

Perhaps when we wash in the morning we could ask who is it who is being washed and who is washing?

*As we wash our ears we could vow to hear well, to
listen well, and to focus on that in each of us which is
the always-already beginninglessly enlightened.*

*As we wash our mouths we could vow to ourselves to speak truth
lovingly throughout the course of the day. We could vow to use
this day wisely to facilitate the realisation of the One-Taste.*

*As we wash our eyes we could vow to see clearly without
prejudice. We could vow to always see the always-already
beginninglessly enlightened nature of all people around
us, despite their stories and because of their stories.*

*As we wash our nostrils and nose we could vow
to know the perfection of all fragrances.*

*As we wash our skin we could vow to touch others
with love and to be touched by what we sense around
us, to open to each moment with an open heart.*

*As we connect with the element of water, we could feel the water
that seventy percent of this body is also made of, in one flow.*

Morning somatic practice

Morning somatic practice is an opportunity for moving prayer, an opportunity for an exploration of the intimacy of body, breath, bio-energy, mind and environment.

Somatic practice is a practice of empowerment, preventative medicine and a celebration of incarnation. Somatic practice will be part of the healing journey and the journey into deeper love and awakening.

Somatic practice is an exploration of openness integrated with strength and woven into optimal function

What does it feel like to be this open?

What does it feel like to be this strong?

Who is it who feels open and strong?

Who is practising?

What is being practised?

Somatic practice is, at its best, an awakening practice. At its simplest it is physical exercise. Each flowing movement of the mind-breath-energy-body mirrors sacred geometry. Each moment is a gateway to realisation, a gateway to the realisation of the always-already inseparability that is reality.

As we awaken to reality then we will not need all our ego defences, or the isolation and withdrawal strategies held up by our unconscious beliefs about separation. The citadel of the self-structure is going to tumble down. Somatic practice prepares for, invites and welcomes this inevitability.

Keeping the body as healthy and well as you can is an act of worship and devotion. A healthy body is, to a degree, a function of a healthy mind and an appreciative heart.

Keeping the bio-electric-magnetic-flow of your separate feeling existence in a state of good enough flow is an act of worship and devotion. A healthy flowing energetic system is a function of a healthy mind and an appreciative heart.

Realising the inherent emptiness of all arising phenomena as the appearance of existence or non-existence is worship and devotion. Knowing the empty as full and the full as empty in each moment is realised mind and heart.

Meeting the Self through the self

It is utterly ironic but it is the self-contraction, the ego, that leads us to the point of jumping off the cliff of rationality. The ego is the key point of leverage between selfishness and opening up to the vast open love of the Self. Either the ego looks down (I'm deliberately using the verticality metaphor here!) into the obsessions and concerns of the small self, or it begins to look up into the unbounded and vast reality of our core identity.

First, you have to get utterly bored and frustrated with being such a selfish, obsessive and small minded being, riddled with narcissistic traits. You have to see enough of your strategies of separation and deceit, manipulation and coercion to want something more. You have to believe there is something more than being just a healthy ego. And have the desire to change and grow.

The neuroses of the ego are the twists of realised energy. The realised energy of your true nature has been distorted through the conditioning you received as a child, and through your culture. This true nature has been twisted through fear into ultimate concern only for one's own welfare, and the welfare of one's ethnic group and culture. Isn't this rather similar to the gang mentality that pervades media stories?

Openness to love becomes jaded through the boundaries we impose on life, so all that remains underneath every opening into love is fear of loss and even more fear and separation. If we study our neuroses and follow their energy deeply enough we will see that every neurotic feeling and thought is bubbling out of the illusion of being a separate self. Once we realise that all our stories and fears are no more than twisted bubbles of dualistic distortion, we have to want more. The alternative is to simply collapse into the post-modern disease of nihilistic desperation, depression or existential crisis.

It is the deep feelings of love and the recognition of underlying consciousness moving through our neuroses and obsessive self-stories that sustains us through dark nights of the soul. These key energies of awakened potential guide us through the dance of shadow and light until we begin to recognise that being nobody is the way to love. When we are happy being nobody, being inconsequential, then we can be somebody.

- *Wisdom teaches us we are nobody.*

- *Love teaches us we are everybody.*

Love and wisdom in action is Engaged Yoga in daily life. When we are love and wisdom in action we act spontaneously in the best possible way for the benefit of all beings, we don't have to contrive it, practising is over. Spontaneously arising goodness for the benefit of all beings now just happens, all the time.

Meditation

Just being good at meditation is fairly pointless.

Being 'good enough' at meditation is fantastic and certainly good enough. Meditation is simply the vehicle, it serves the purpose of awakening.

Meditation changes how brains work. In conjunction with reflection, somatic practice, breath-work, and study and service in the world for the benefit of all beings, meditation offers us a powerful transformational tool.

When the brain has changed, when the perceptual position has shifted from self to Self as Vedanta might say, or from self-ishness to Buddha nature, then what use is the vehicle?

A practice of fifteen minutes of meditation practised twice daily is better than a long sit once a week. Regularity and strategy are far more important than intensity.

In The Book of Purpose you will find strategies for the rapid development of meditational practice so that it facilitates the transparency of the self-contraction.

Practise Dream Yoga as well, this will also accelerate the process of meditation. Somatic Yoga also enhances and accelerates the process of meditation.

Practising regularly, wisely and well, reaps results. Practising badly, with lack of regularity, doubt, grandiosity, or other delusions, reaps more suffering.

Meditation is firstly cultivation of the witness consciousness and then dissolution of the witness consciousness into cosmic consciousness and authentic freedom.

Practice with integrity and diligence, vowing to awaken and vowing to use the energy of practice for the benefit of all beings everywhere. Then the practice is vital, energised and sparkles through the rest of your life in unexpected ways.

With honest and diligent practice the clarity arising through meditation flows into the period of post-meditation and manifests as action in the world. Remember, yoga is ultimately love and wisdom in action. Through practice, meditation and action become one flow of clarity.

How will you act in the world from a place of meditative insight?

How will you act in the world from a place of realised inseparability?

Who will act?

Mantra

Mantra literally means mind expansion, and can also mean mind protection.

• It offers the expansion of small mind into cosmic mind.

• It offers protection from one's own mundane and tedious self-story.

Mantra is first to be practised aloud. This needs to occur often enough to get the mantra charged with vitality and for the mind and body systems to become deeply familiar with its vibration. The mantra becomes neurologically embedded.

Later, mantra can be practised as a whisper on the breath.

Lastly, mantra can be practised silently in the mind whilst deepening the breath.

Mantra is energy, it is vibration.

Formal practices of mantra are done sitting with a beginning and an end to the practice period. They will be done in specific settings such as shrine rooms, meditation spaces, and so on.

Informal practices are where the mantra spontaneously generates itself, or it can be consciously generated. Informal practices can occur literally anywhere in any situation. Informal practices are rooted in formal practices. Silent practice is rooted in audible practice. The mantra slowly gains power through repetition.

Focusing life energy and attention on the mantra given by one's teacher, instead of on one's relentless self-story, is a developmental delight. Mantra can help us focus on aspects of our being where we need to grow and develop.

A person who can stop cerebral noise, cease involvement at will with inner dialogue and rest in the inner space with only the vibration of the mantra, is a Yogin-Yogini.

The person who can then allow the mantra to softly reside in their consciousness and then utterly rest in boundless emptiness, is a Yogin-Yogini.

The one who knows emptiness, and vibrates this through the mantra back into form, is a Yogin-Yogini.

Weaving emptiness, energy and form as inseparability through mantra, love and realisation is the play of the Yogin-Yogini.

Devotion and Worship

Devotion to the essence of life is Biophilia. We practice bio-philia whenever we celebrate and find gratitude and devotion for the essence of all life.

Devotion (bhakti) is a powerful and beautiful path to self-transcendence. In the yoga of devotion the practitioner connects, initially outwardly, to a Being-ness perceived as far greater, more wonderful, and more deserving than one's separate, limited, body-mind experience.

What is one to be devoted to?

Who is devoted to what?

• Some worship the infinite and all pervasive formlessness of the absolute.

• Some worship the sacred essence of life.

• Some worship the awesome vastness of the universe and beyond.

• Some worship their teacher, their Guru.

• Some worship their lover as the essence of the divine.

• Some worship their ishta-devata, their chosen deity form that becomes their personal avenue to transcendence.

Deity forms are used in many cultures and are often anthropomorphic or historical beings, as is common in Christianity, Hinduism and Buddhism.

Whatever approach you utilise, you really need to believe it, enjoy it, and cultivate the neuro-chemicals of bliss. Realise that devotion takes you out of your self.

Most people bow in worship unconsciously

People commonly bow to some limited principle or pseudo-deity. Usually the pseudo-deity is fear, money, power, sexual charisma, superficial beauty (symmetry and surfaces), youth or status. Since most of us bow to something unconsciously anyway, we might as well make it conscious and productive in terms of transcendence.

Through the yoga of devotion we can begin to cultivate the neurology of wonder, deep love and connection. In this space of love and connection the practitioner may begin to see the truth of their deeper nature beyond the limited self-construct. Then, through surrender to this greater whole, one begins to experience truth beyond the ego and slowly becomes this greater possibility.

Shrines help many people achieve this. We create a spectrum of devotion with whatever our shrine represents as being the apogee of affection, devotion and truth. When we set up a shrine in our house and place objects on it to represent truth, love wisdom and the essence of life, we can practice and generate devotion with relative ease.

Because we can become so immune to awe and beauty, so switched into mundanity that we close our minds and hearts to the fundamental juice, richness and sheer bliss of existence, a shrine can act as an anchor to hold our awe and affection.

Devotion can be a naturally arising sense of pure gratitude
for every arising moment, no matter what is happening.

In the beginning, for contemporary beings who are caught up with consumption and instant gratification, conscious devotion can be uncomfortable, even impossible.

Babies, puppies, and other beautiful beings open the hearts of some. Suffering and pain opens the hearts of others. If nothing else works then, as you die, you will open.

Either way, the heart has to open.

The practices of devotion are methods for opening the heart during life, and through this the mind.

Devotion, celebration, and gratitude go hand in hand. This trio support each other and assist the heart to open.

Celebration can be practised individually or collectively. Collective celebrations, whether ritual or spontaneous, bring communities of practitioners into a deeper synergy and engagement.

Let us celebrate together as communities of love, why not?

Why not be utterly devoted to love in all its dances, totally devoted to wisdom and truth, fully devoted to the deepest freedom for all beings everywhere?

How about being a devotee of conscious evolution, a bio-philiac?

We are relational beings. We are never not in relationship. Growing and nourishing our mutual relationships is the work of conscious evolution, as Engaged Yoga.

Seeing others through the eyes of love

them, and in your self.

People often act out of fear, unconscious programming, and distorted views. From feeling like a self-sense which is isolated and different to the rest of the universe, the root feeling that arises is fear, or even unmitigated terror.

Distortion of the primary life energy leads to fear. Life energy that is really one with the flow of totality, whilst also experiencing the face of separateness, tends to get warped solely into the experience of separateness. This results in the patterns and emotions of separateness that include fear, hatred, anger, jealousy, envy, blame, shame, and toxic guilt.

For sure, people mostly live from their patterns and carry out behaviours that increase the collective burden of suffering and pain. Yet, underneath all of this, every single being is a 'Buddha to be'. Inside the most nefarious and vile acts, somewhere deep inside is a 'Buddha to be' wrapped in twisted sheaths of fear and pain.

Yoga sees this clearly. If we love the Buddha within whilst being clear that the patterns of fear and pain are simply unskilful distortions of life energy, we invite the processes of liberation.

Try doing this all of the time, every day, all day. Why not?
And then question who is doing this?

Maybe your enlightened expectation, your realisation of love and wisdom in the core of all beings will help bring this out in

INTERACTION

Eating

Your body knows what it needs to eat. If you listen carefully it will tell you, it really will.

- Don't eat to cover feelings or to find comfort.

- Don't eat because it's there.

- Don't eat because it's mealtime.

- Don't eat because others are eating.

- Don't eat because your diet says you have to.

- Eat because you're hungry and your body needs it.

How about only eating because you're hungry and your body needs sustenance?

Now, enjoy the taste, really enjoy it!

Now, make your food beautiful, it's a visual feast isn't it?

Totally enjoy the smell and fragrance.
What does the aroma tell you?

If you can, eat with your fingers so you involve the sense of touch too, feel your food, how is this?

Getting all the senses involved gives you a sensual and sensory relationship with your food.

Love your food.
Offer gratitude to the interdependent web each time you eat.

Best to not eat highly processed commercialised food, it's not really food. Best eat organic, because, if grown well, it can be kinder to our environment and our bodies, and they are not separate are they? Organic pricing can be prohibitive though for poorer people. What can we do to help with this?

Let's pay attention to air miles until we get some seriously carbon-footprint-free green aviation fuel. Will you choose to purchase out of season fruits and vegetables shipped for miles around the planet with the idea that it's good for you?

If it's not good for the planet can it really be good for you?

This may mean we have to pay attention more to what grows on our own land, in our own neighbourhood. Can we do this?

What changes do you have to make to your diet to facilitate a carbon neutral diet?

A challenge for all vegans and vegetarians - eat only what grows within a thirty kilometre radius from your home.
A challenge for all meat eaters - kill, gut, skin and butcher the animal you are wanting to eat. Make sure it ran around freely before you do this. If you can't do this maybe don't eat it!

Food is medicine!

No one diet fits all. Depending on your context, climate, condition, cultural history and constitution you will require different or specific foods.

Many people will try to tell you what you need to be eating and why. Many people will come up with convincing narratives to justify their beliefs, we won't to do that. You're going to have to work it out yourself through inquiry and study of your own system. You're going to have to listen to inner feedback and work with your relationship to the environment.

What medicine do you need?

What dietary relationship do you have with the environment?

So let's celebrate and enjoy our food and keep checking in with the carbon inquiry and the ethics of diet. Remember, eating is interaction, it is relationship, it's Engaged Yoga.

Working Life

What do you do to generate your income?

What is the relationship between your income generation and your environmental ethics?

What is the relationship between your income generation and your yogic practice and the ethical bases of that practice?

How does the creation of your income affect other people?

Does the production of your income require other people or other life-forms to suffer?

Right livelihood has always been a concern for yoga practitioners. We have always sought to pay skilful attention to the consequences of all our actions whilst sustaining joy, fun, beauty and love.

This is, and always has been, a tightrope walk that requires consideration, patience, and the capacity to work with paradox.

We have to ask ourselves how our actions in the world create greater joy and openness for ourselves and all other beings. These sorts of worthy inquiries are a part of our practice that really facilitates the movement of yogic realisation, or superconsciousness, into everyday life.

How does your working life balance your practice life and your home life?

How does your working life support your practice and your evolution into awakening?

Are you following your calling with your work life, is it your purpose or just a way of making a living?

What is purpose?

Is purpose something you craft?

In our view, purpose is a heartfelt feeling of aptness, yet it is something we craft and evolve through the course of our lives.

What are you willing to do to follow your purpose, to move with your calling?

How will you make a good living whilst following your deepest hearts calling?

What are the costs to your sense of joy and wellbeing if you sacrifice your deepest calling at the shrine of convenience, profit and convention?

There may be no getting it 'right'. There will probably always be attention needed to facilitate the balance of right livelihood and income generation. There may always be new energies to move with and new concerns to pay attention to. Each new challenge will offer its opportunities for growth though.

How will you stay open, loving and joyful amidst the clash and thunder of conflict, chaos, collapse, and reconstruction?

How do you best rise to the challenges of growth? How will you manage the yoga of working life?

Wealth, Shopping, Consumption and Freedom

The Book of Purpose, the yoga of real wealth has some helpful strategies to look at real wealth, consumption, and financial habits.

People still commonly buy consumer items in an endeavour to feel secure, in control, approved of, loved, connected, and having an identity, being someone.

This form of consumerism is infinite because it never works more than temporarily. It is like sticking band-aids on a major haemorrhage. It is looking for love, security, truth, unicity, and identity in all the wrong places. If the places we look for these qualities are all impermanent, the result will be impermanent. Consumer goods are superbly impermanent, even the best of them.

The worst of them are almost instant landfill.

Money is fabricated by the economic authorities such as the International Monetary Fund, World Bank and other institutions. Money no longer means anything, it is 'fiat' money, it is imagined into existence.

Despite this the consequences of 'not having' include hunger, thirst, homelessness, and destitution. The global economic system clearly controls the 'have nots' through fear.

Without buying into this system or its fear-based strategies of social control, if we spend what we don't have, it leads us into debt.

Debt is not freedom, it's economic servitude.

Systems built around controlling people through fear and debt are not interested in freedom, but in economic servitude and dependence.

Are we not seeking to step from ignorance to consciousness, from reflexive habits to freedom, and from feudal servitude to collective freedom?

Buying from ego desires, all of which are ultimately fear based, will ultimately be unfulfilling.

It is worth understanding that 'buying' simply means accessing resources. We are seeking to access resources which we are using for the greatest good of all, and so buying 'stuff' is legitimate. We need access to resources!

If we buy (access) what we really need, what we really want, what serves our growth and through this the greater good, this then leads us to authentic freedom, individually and collectively.

As the cost of extracting oil and other strategic resources from the earth rises, as the cost of energy and production thereby rises, then recycling becomes worthwhile at last and we can no longer buy into the myth of infinite and relentless growth.

This planet really does have limits to growth. Limits to growth means that an economic system based on the infinitely expanding production of consumer goods is unsustainable. If we don't pay attention to the balance, the homoeostasis needed, then the system crashes into unsustainability.

The enlightened choice is to live, buy, consume, use, reuse and recycle as sustainably as we can.

Giving a generous percentage of our income to worthy causes keeps us in a mindset of generosity and flow. The mindset of generosity, sharing, and flow is real wealth. Anything else is simply grasping at 'stuff'.

Spending only what we can afford teaches patience and contentment. This is a powerful practice.

Collaborative works of sharing resources such as in credit unions and other collective and ethical wealth sharing practices really do serve the cause of freedom.

Renouncing supporting unethical bankers, their vast bonuses and lifestyles of greed is also a good practice.

Knowing more fully who you are liberates you.
Core-identity, really knowing ourselves as freedom, authentic freedom, wisdom and the deepest love, liberates us.

Since you are love, where can you look for what you already are?

There is nowhere else to go for love, you simply give and serve as love. Since you are authentic freedom, unbound, unconstrained, where do you need to look for freedom? Nowhere? Freedom is always here, always now.

Knowing more fully who you are liberates you!

• It liberates you from pathological spending behaviours.

• It moves you into growth-oriented behaviour.

• It allows you to use money for your, and our, higher needs of growth, contribution and service.

Spending consciously on personal growth and development can facilitate your expansion into greater wellbeing, greater awareness, greater connection and abundance. This will then facilitate greater wellbeing and abundance for all.
Spending intelligently on cultivating your talents and pursuing your passions, so that you can offer and share these in the world more fully, will help make this a more abundant planet.
Spending wisely on being joyous, on celebrations, events, experiences, or things that bring you, your loved ones and others joy, is a rich way to use our wealth.

Recognise the incredible wealth we receive daily and celebrating the massive abundance of this universe. We choose to cultivate the attitude of gratitude at every opportunity, until it becomes merely a way of being.

Money gives three things…
• Access to resources

• Space for choice

• Something we exchange our life energy for

These are of course fantastic, to a degree…
The other things that money gives, such as feelings of possession, security, status and identity are all rather low-level ego

desires. They are merely temporary states that serve only the cause of deeper separation and human suffering.

There is nothing wrong with being ethically wealthy and using wealth for the cause of conscious evolution and radikal freedom, is there?

The question is, are you awake enough, wise enough, loving enough not to be seduced by the power that wealth can confer?

We trust so...

Transport

We travel. We try to go by train and public transport as often as possible. Christopher runs his personal vehicle on bio-diesel made from recycled vegetable oil.

Yet we live in a world where almost all transport infrastructures are fossil fuel dependent.

How do any of us get around with any real level of carbon sensitivity when global infrastructure is so confined?

What alternatives are available to us?

Could we develop mag-lev[10] vehicular pods that sit on rails during inter-city transits and drop into an individualised mode, running on solar electric, when inside an urban environment?

Can we use trains more and power these with sustainably produced electric?

How about more mag-lev trains that have less moving parts?

How about the hybrid airplanes running on bio-fuels that have already been tested in prototype?

How can developers and investors be encouraged to pay attention to exciting new and old possibilities?

Sustainable aviation fuel has been made with the help of blue

green algae, why are we not investing large scale in this?

Why are airlines not insisting on its development?

How can we be more active in demanding cleaner transportation that is fossil fuel free?

What are the most effective strategies to reduce fossil fuel dependence and encourage transport providers to come up with the goods, fossil-fuel-free transport for all?

Obviously walking and cycling are part of the way forward.

Why does it appear that industry leaders are not paying attention to cutting edge developments that can lead to a more sustainable world?

How can we help them to pay attention and prioritise ecological concerns over profit alone?

How can we show how serious we are about this and help governments and industry to understand that it is in their and our interest to be proactive in investing in sustainable development?

How will we encourage city planners to do more than token sustainability programs?

Do residential parking zones really solve the awful problems of congestion, or are they just another fancy urban tax?

---

10. Magnetic levitation as used in trains. Imagine cars that run on mag-lev rails, just tap your destination into the onboard computer, watch a movie and come off at your exit. Your personalised pod then runs on electric power. How creative can we be as we dream the sustainable future into existence? This sort of technology is becoming highly available.

How do we resolve urban congestion?

How can we help them to get some energy and money behind making all cities green and make all city transport and inter-city transport completely integrated and sustainable?

We have the technology. We really do. Yet we appear to lack the incentive, the relevant investment and the concerted political will.

What is our role in encouraging these three key missing elements?

Remember vast sums of money are spent in weapons technology and weapons purchase and use annually.

Why are these resources not being spent on sustainability instead?

We have the money and the technology, yet where is the investment and the concerted, focused political will to action the generation and provision of sustainable transportation?

Surely it is time?

Energy production and consumption

For society to survive we need energy. Whether the energy comes from burning wood, coal, from nuclear fusion or fission, or from the wind and sun we still need energy.

If we look into world history we find that pre-industrial societies all gained their energy from slavery. Every culture built their world on slavery of some kind or another. Slavery is still happening, whether its wage slavery, sexual slavery through human traffic, workers in sweat shops, or mistreated migrant workers building vast castles to commerce in desert landscapes for fossil fuel magnates.

Given we don't want a return to greater levels of slavery, given we have to give up our addiction to burning fossil fuels for energy, where are we going to get our energy from?

Nuclear is getting cleaner, fission is getting cleaner and there is the possibility of fusion.

Do we go nuclear?

The post-fission cleaning up process is still highly problematic though. We don't have effective ways to deal with all the waste and it is totally unfair to leave that problem to future generations, isn't it?

In our view, we should not use technologies that require us to indebt and burden our descendants. What's your view?

Solar concentrating mirrors, better quality photovoltaics along with some wind power, some wave power, some hydro-power, some geo-thermal, some bio-mass conversion would allow global energy requirements to be met quite easily.

Why are we not doing it?
Where are the vested interests blocking such development?
Can these blockages be easily resolved?
What will it take to shift them?

Then there is the possibility that has also been well tested of growing blue-green algae that will both break down our waste products and purify waste water as well as giving the means for creating fuel. Blue-green algae produce huge amounts of oil, all of it carbon-neutral.

Of course there is also wave power, hydro-electric, geothermal power, bio-mass conversion and so many more ways of generating relatively clean electricity. With a mosaic of techniques of generation techniques we could easily provide our global energy needs. Why aren't we doing it?

Along with renewable power sourcing, surely we need to pay attention to energy conservation?

Efficient insulation, sustainable and well-engineered cooling systems, and attention to all new building design as well as old structure conversion to appropriate eco standards could be a priority, couldn't it?

Why is it not a priority?
Why is it not happening?

What is needed to make it happen more fully?

In what ways are we prepared to reduce our energy consumption? How will we build a culture of appropriately lower energy consumption?

Given the trillions of dollars spent annually on weapons provision and warfare, would this money be more wisely spent on providing sustainable energy production systems, or are we missing something?

Reduce – Reuse – Recycle - Reinvent

Reduce, reuse, recycle is the great ecological and systemic mantra within our culture of mass consumption. This is so important, yet so taken for granted.

'Reinvent' is our addition.

If we took things back to the drawing board and insisted on using the latest technology we could make products using a fraction of the resources and energy required to build, maintain and run them. Factor Four the report to the Club of Rome in 1997 by Ernst Von Weizacker, Amory B. Lovins and L. Hunter Lovins pointed this out so successfully.

Why are our production techniques so caught up in inefficient strategies?

What role do vested interests play?

In Factor Four everyday items such as light bulbs, motor cars, washing machines and fridges are redesigned using current technology so as to reduce by at least a factor of four (that's a quarter) the fuel required to build and run such items. A simple example would be electro-magnetic brakes on cars that don't need to rely on friction, therefore no wear and tear.

We have the technology, using solar concentrating mirrors, to produce all the energy this planet needs.

We believe it should be illegal to make energy that is unsustainably sourced. The production of globally sustainable energy could be achieved using a fraction of the amount of money spent on arms and weaponry worldwide.

How will we as a species stop squabbling and fighting over resources?

What role can we play in this transition?

All packaging could, by law, or by financial incentive, be reduced to the bare minimum and be recyclable.

Manufacturers could also be required to pay for any ecological costs of the products they make.

Instead of pushing costs onto the consumer or more usually the tax-payer, manufacturers could be required to deal with the systemic chaos created through using ecologically unsound packaging and manufacturing systems, couldn't they?

Many industries, such as mining, are becoming much more responsible and creative in pre-empting the environmental damage that our activities can create. We need much, much more proactive attention to the environmental consequences of all our human activities.

The bare minimum we can do as Engaged Yoga practitioners is to reduce all unnecessary consumption, reuse all materials possible, and recycle everything else. Ideally there would be virtually nothing left to go into landfills.

Could we collectively support and push through political process via the power of our wallets, votes and action, thereby generating greater effectiveness and awareness of the four key processes of reduction, re-use, recycling and reinventing?

Could we push for intelligently reinvented products that use state of the art technology?

Could we support technology that minimises the use of energy and resources for the production, maintenance, use and recycling of all the products we use in our lives?

As Engaged Yoga practitioners we could also be proactive in encouraging recalcitrant leaders of governments, media and industry to pay attention to systemics.

Systemic realisation in yoga is the deep kinaesthetic knowledge of our total inter-relationship with all life-form. We are dependent on bees. Remember, all of life is interdependent. Bees in fact would survive better without us, not so easy the other way around.

Substantial research clearly indicates that our fossil fuel burning activities are disturbing water systems, air systems, planetary thermals, and are putting the lives of cold-blooded invertebrates such as bees at stake.

Lets pay attention!

Are there any governments that have good clear and proactive environmental records?

Despite the political appearances and green-wash prevalent on this planet, there is no concerted effort to create a real global council that will seek and utilise expert opinion to manage and steward our planet.

Decisions continue to be made as if every nation were separate from every other nation, as if the environmental degradation caused by one country doesn't affect us all. Realising inseparability, greater numbers of us (humans) will be paying attention and really work together on these key issues of our time.

Our belief is that we need to build a proactive and awakened global culture of stewardship where all tribes, all nations, all peoples work harmoniously to create mutual wellbeing and mutual prosperity

What actions can we take to co-create the awakened culture that will create a habitable planet for our children and our children's children?

What actions will we now be taking to co-create the awakened culture that will create a habitable planet for our children and our children's children?

Medicine and Health Care

All those who have a relationship with an intelligent yogic practice know that at best it is a preventative, rejuvenative and therapeutic medicine that can prevent, heal or help many health related problems.

The body is constantly seeking balance and healing. It consistently seeks balance or homeostasis within both the capacity and limits of its evolution.

Yoga practitioners know through direct experience the relationship between mind, breath, feelings, body and environment.

Wouldn't it be fabulous if this subjective experience was, at last, taken seriously and became objective through the inquiry of empiricism?

We know the power of mind focused through belief. The most tested contemporary medicine is placebo. Researchers have even tested placebos when people know they are placebos and if they are told the placebo worked for other people then it still works.

We really would do well to empirically test the power of belief and suggestion and start using these powers of the mind to prevent and heal medical problems.

Asian flow medicines, exemplified by yoga, Ayurveda, martial arts, traditional Chinese medicine, and all their variants, keep their practitioners in high states of optimal wellbeing. Through the study of factors that work best to sustain optimal wellbeing we could cultivate a global culture of preventative and rejuvenative medicine.

A culturally approved preventative medicine could save millions of dollars, euros, pounds, yen, yuan, rupees, or whatever currency you prefer. Prevention is always better than cure. Curative medicine is much more expensive.

Contemporary curative medicine is mostly wonderful and if either of us had a damaging car crash we would demand the attentions of a contemporary doctor not an Ayurvedic practitioner.

What else do we need to pay attention to with medicine and wellbeing?

the Path to Awakening

*Sexual energy is how we all got here. It is
the primary driving force of life.*

The Indian traditions, the Christian tradition, the Islamic
tradition, and the Buddhist tradition have for the most part,
for the last two thousand or more, either made sexuality
wrong, criminal and low or sought to control it's expressions
through rigid and oppressive rules. Many cultures and societies
still do this.

Some religious views on sexuality suggest it distracts us from
knowing divinity. Some religious views suggest that exploring
sexuality makes us more 'animal', but then are we not actually
mammals?

Some religious views on sexuality suggest that sexual activity
other than for procreation is demonic.

What are your thoughts?

All patriarchal religions and their associated spiritual traditions seek to control sexuality, seek to control women, and seek
to minimise the developmental potential of our full ecstatic
sexual response.

All patriarchal religions make all of our basic juicy mammalian existence taboo.

Engaged Yoga suggests that our basic juicy mammalian existence is the path to awakening, the way of a juicy Engaged

Yoga, and the way of a juicy Engaged Yogini or Yogi.

Certainly, in medieval times the pleasures of the flesh were compromised by the horrific and largely incurable sexually transmitted diseases. Peri-natal mortality was also rife with horrific consequences. Simple toothache could kill you. And that is one of the reasons Yoga arose in medieval India as a profound preventative health practice.

With all the suffering of life before the advent of modern medicine it must have appeared as if life itself were a sexually transmitted disease. It is no surprise that many of the spiritual traditions from this time were life denying and ascendant. Up with God is good and is safe, down here in the flesh is perpetual struggle and suffering, isn't it?.

Now we know different. Now we understand bacteria, viruses and we craft medicines that really do make a difference, despite the views of many palaeo-romantics. We really are in the Golden Age, this is as good as it gets, and we can collectively make it even better.

We always have had shadow to work with and process. We always will have shadow to work with and process.

The simple question is, are we willing to do the work?

From the view of Engaged Yoga we start where we are. Engaged Yoga is a celebration of where we are as the starting point of any practice. All the juices, desires, flows and varying manifestations of mammalian existence are invited, welcomed, appreciated, and celebrated.

The base of development is the acceptance and appreciation of our mammalian physical nature. All those clichéd teachings that suggest we are 'spiritual beings' having a human experience can be seen as the pathologies they are. They provide an 'out', they are a running away from the complexities of incarnation.

Now Feel…
Feel where you are, be fully present with all of your emotional, physical, energetic existence first. The idea we are 'spiritual beings' is just that, an idea.

Know yourself first as juice and meat, as body, as feelings, as a complexity of thoughts. Now look deeply into and celebrate all aspects of your existence. Is there still need to run like a scared rabbit for the "Beam me up Scotty" style of spirituality.

Many people who consider themselves to be spiritual are perhaps neurotic, deeply scared of feeling, deeply scared of living, and scared of fully relating. Scared like this one might run for what one considers to be a sanctuary, a refuge, a place beyond flesh, beyond juice, beyond feeling, beyond the complexities of the self-construct and its tales. But running in this way doesn't work, it is simply spiritual by-passing.

Spiritual by-passing cannot yield realisation, awakening, knowledge or happiness. Spiritual by-passing only creates an unhappy, fearful fugitive from incarnation, a fugitive who is ignoring the key elements that will enable authentic freedom.

These keys are the body and its limitations, the feelings and their demands, and the mind and its stories. These are the initial keys we have to realising freedom. We ignore them at our peril.

When we understand we are our body, we
can then know we are not just that.

When we understand we are our feelings, we
can then know we are not just those.

When we understand we are our thoughts, we
can then know we are not just these.

Now we can look deeply into our core-identity.

From the view of Engaged Yoga sexual energy is both sacred and beautiful.

Mutual sexual expression is a healthy and vibrant sharing of love. Sexuality is also part of the path of awakening. As part of the path of awakening, turning arising sexual energy into whole-body ecstasy can easily facilitate movement beyond the self-story. Receiving and giving, the sharing of 'Bodylove', is a very important and loving Engaged Yoga practice.

Yogic massage in conjunction with this loving consensual sexuality celebrates and deepens our experience in full residence and of full appreciation for this physical incarnation, as it is. Such practice honours the primary life energies that move through us, as us. Such perspectives of honouring and appreciating the flesh, feelings, and life energy flow does not deny our deeper essence as pure being. It simply suggests that celibacy is not necessarily the best way to know our 'essence' as pure being.

Sexual Yogas are profound when worked with effectively, and when sexual energy is completely in service to the heart and to the deepening in love of those involved, and to all beings everywhere. Sexual energy channelled through the heart and up to the crown and beyond opens one into the field of totality. Lovemaking can be an awakening practice. Like any art it has to be cultivated. We could spend time learning and sharing this art as this art itself, of itself, and of how it can and does spread the vibrations of love. As far as we are concerned, the more loved up people there are on this planet, the better.

Loved up, loving and physically aware contact can also cultivate deeper awareness and celebration of the physical-emotional relationships with our fellow being. Engaging with this encourages the co-creation and awakening of respectful and mutually consenting relationship.

Many religiously inclined yogic teachings, as previously mentioned, are in essence ascendant and masculist, and focus on withdrawal from physical contact. Such teachings either ignore or negate physical contact and sexuality or push them into the shadows of taboo.

Authentic love and freedom has no taboos. Authentic love accepts all of our functions and welcomes them all as practices of celebratory awareness and consciousness. The eyes of love recognises everything, absolutely everything, as Divinity. From this view all conscious actions and behaviours, particularly those that promote loving, consenting behaviour are fuel for finding the presence of awareness in and as the ground of all.

Confusion arises from the masculist misunderstanding of

lust for loving sexuality. Many 'religious style' yogic teachers were celibate, or living in cultural constraints that really did not honour sexuality. Many never experienced any deep loving sexuality. Many may well have experienced lust or libidinous sex-drive and, scared of its power, pushed it into the shadows. Many still do.

Loving mutual sexuality and it's bright components comprise:

- *Clear and open communication*

- *Beautiful lust*

- *Physical play*

- *Fun*

- *Mutual respect*

- *Creative sexual expression*

- *Deep listening*

- *Engaged consenting spontaneity*

- *Heart opening love*

- *Blissful ecstatic openness to the other*

Far from living in the shadows and the realm of repression, these components rest fully and joyfully in the light of aware ness and consciousness, through a resonant practice of Engaged

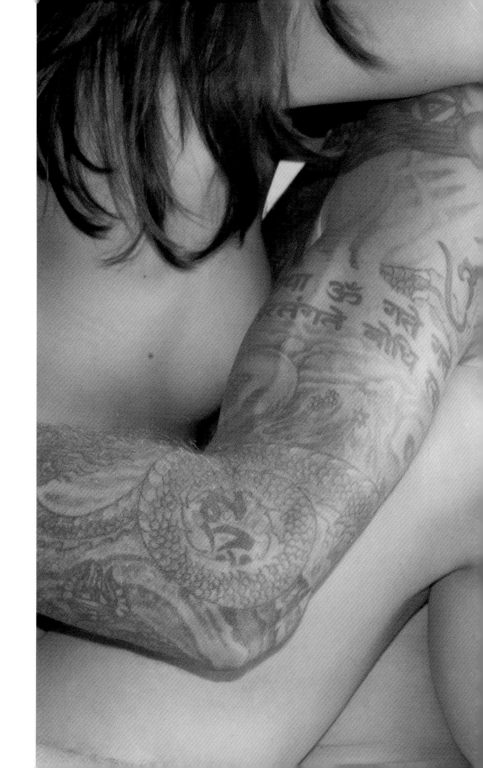

Yoga.

To engage in free loving Sexual Yoga, all that is needed is loving, consenting adults who are willing to explore, with awareness, polarised energies through sexual desire and love and find the expressions and experience of union within this dance.

In a culture that is historically riddled with:

• Oppressive religious conditioning

• Disrespect, objectification and control of women

• Pathological conditioning of men

• Disrespect for women's choices

• Teaching children sexuality through ignorance and pornography

• Criminalisation of aspects of sexual exploration and expression

• Predominance of pain and suffering over the neurology of pleasure and bliss

... then loving aware sexuality as yoga that is open, aware and celebratory is surely an absolute necessity?

Reclaiming touch, sensuality and loving sexuality is a valid and powerful approach to finding the presence of awareness in everyday life.

Cultivating conscious relationship, playfulness, energetic exploration and a powerful and beautiful lived expression of love is a crucial practice in our gender befuddled, prurient, and abusively commercial culture.

Healthy sexual practice and vibrant lovemaking are also a profound part of the way we celebrate being fully alive and of experiencing the essential flow of life-force that manifests through sexuality, within our loving relationships.

Consent is an ongoing process, necessary in each moment and from moment to moment. This is an aspect of clear and attentive communication that provides a loving foundation for the relationship, which allows each participant to explore their reality with the other with loving kindness and awareness.

Unlike some monastic spiritual traditions, we simply do not believe that the highest lifeform on this planet is a celibate male.

Not recognising the supremacy of this orientation liberates the realm of loving sexuality as a valid and powerful expression of love and consciousness.

Unless celibacy is naturally arising and offers a deeper understanding of the possibilities of love it is in our view simply an imposed perversion that simply frustrates or distorts life energy flow.

Heart focused loving simply means you know each other as equal in love. Whatever your sexual orientation and however you choose to lovingly engage and explore is up to you. Heart focused lovemaking is about growing into and sustaining love on every level and through all of your life experience.

Heart focused lovemaking can free one physically and emotionally, generate and channel prana flow, liberate mind function and take us beyond pleasure into real bliss and emptiness conjoined. Bliss and emptiness conjoined is realisation, it is the path of awakening.

With the realisation of the profound emptiness-bliss of all arising phenomena one can know all nervous system sensations as empty. Remember that empty doesn't mean void, devoid or nothingness, empty is empty of conceptual limitation, empty of self-sense, empty of definition, empty of emptiness.

Empty is totally full. Emptiness is the essence of form and form is none other than emptiness.

When we finally grasp this then we can fully understand what love means. So when we know all our nervous system sensations as empty, they can all be felt, seen, tasted for what they are and left to move.

Nothing is grasped, as there is no one to do the grasping and nothing to be grasped. There is only beautiful flow. Seeing, tasting and knowing flow we are also pure Being as flow...

From this realisation, and with good somatic awareness and bodylove then one learns to expand one's energetic field into blissful radiance.

Practices of lovemaking are then offered in sacrifice, as one resolves one's neurological separation, one's self-sense into bliss-emptiness.

The energy of orgasm and bliss is cultivated, spread throughout one's energy field and expanded into the universe with no boundaries. Illusions dissolve.

Engaged Yoga celebrates loving committed relationship, however you consensually choose to do this, as a superior path of development. Will you engage with a single consort in intimate embrace or will you choose to co-create loving scenarios where the appearance of monogamy is not the norm?

Most people find that being deeply successful at intimacy in monogamy is required first otherwise the tendency is to slide into non-heart focused lovemaking, into a masquerade of intimacy that is really some sort of sexual addiction.

Either way, continuously learning, learning what it is to balance the rich passion of erotic love with the deep compassion of universal love, we can joyfully explore the juicy richness and wealth of being alive as consciously sexual, consciously loving, highly aware beings, rising and expanding in love as love.

Switch On...

Switched on lovers totally honor each other. Totally!
They worship each other at the bio-philiac shrine of the
holy life breath, the dancing heart, the sparkling mind, the
pulsing emotions and the juicy vibrant genitals. We bow and
kiss, and we dance in bliss in each mundane moment...
Aroma and fragrance becomes sweet as each opens in
love as love and all bodily flows are known as holy.
Taste is pure delight as we know what we
taste is the one taste of divinity.
We know that what we see as the shape, curve,
wrinkle and line is the landscape of love as story... As
the play of time and space, the divine as flow.
We feel the deep essence of unicity, one as two, two as one,
each in all, the all as each, not as an idea but as a felt reality.

When the breath and energy flows unite and each others
story dissolves into this moment of bliss, this moment of love,
then the juicy play of love is just life loving itself, as us.
Sound arises as the sonorous song of energy, flowing as feeling and
dancing as unadulterated native response to this moment…

A switched on woman simply refuses to do duality
ever again, it is the pit of duality or it is life as
love. This choice arises in each moment…
A switched on man does the same… Chooses
reality, the inseparable, over his story.
A switched on woman sees the whole phenomenal world as
her lover, she is always rising and expanding in love.
As switched on man sees the whole phenomenal world as
his lover, he is always rising and expanding in love.

Eventually these habits, moving through super-
nature, become nature again, after the conditioning
of culture and the lies of history are dissolved.
The wild woman is free, the wild man is free. Not as primitive
reptiles or bestial grunting mammals, each seeking to gratify
and satisfy alone, but as evolving conscious mammals.
Mammals that are the play of divine co-evolution, co-creation,
evolving through self-reflection, through self-realization into
the bio-philiac wonder of manifold life deeply known as
unified, life loving itself, dancing as itself. Pure Being.

The holy triad of erotic, domestic and spiritual, become one
simple flow for the switched on lovers of life.

Pregnancy and Birthing

Conception is the beginning of yoga. Being in the womb and being born are the next stages in each life, in the development of awakened and free beings. The experiences received in the womb and during birthing affect the development of each child. The level of love a mother feels in her world, for herself and for her unborn child affect these crucial early phases of development.

We know that the hypo-thalamic-pituitary axis (the HPA), is set up in the first six months of life. This HPA is the core line of endocrine glands along the midline of the body that determine our basic chemical response to life circumstances. These glands release metabolic hormones, stress hormones, and sexual hormones. Authentic yoga seeks to balance these glands later in life.

When a baby is held, loved, nourished, cared for and is helped with its emotional management then these glands then set at an optimal level. If the foetus and infant experience un-love, stress and fear then these glands are set up to manage a world of fear and un-love.

Babies cannot self-regulate, they cannot calm and comfort themselves. This comfort and emotional regulation needs to be offered to them by loving adults.

Old school behaviours of letting children cry themselves to sleep simply riddle the developing brain with toxic quantities of stress hormones whilst setting the HPA up for a life of anxiety, uncertainty and the feelings of separation and other mental health problems.

Being riddled with stress hormones at an early age predisposes the brain for poor internal communication. The part that feels and the part that can express feelings will be unable to communicate effectively. Dysfunctional unloving parenting exposes the baby to a risk of emotional illiteracy and problematic relationships, probably like its parents.

Brains riddled with stress hormones at an early age are pre-wired with parts of the brain that are lacking in pleasure receptors, they cannot feel pleasure in the same way as others who have these pleasure receptors.

Brains riddled with stress hormones at an early age are also set up for ineffective concentration.

Brains grown in toxic environments act as if they are faced with constant threat and at risk of danger. Such brains are always on hyper-alert for the next threat. Is this the way to live life fully?

Babies are 'tribal animals', they need to be near their significant loving elders (parents, grandparents, siblings, etc), to be seen, and to develop optimal emotional and mental function.

Being seen and responded to helps the infant build its neuro-synapses. The baby brain is building its neurological network for at least the first five years of life. Having its preverbal communications and emotional world fully responded to in consistently loving ways is crucial for optimal human functioning.

Loving attentive significant elders are the ones who can understand these communications. Leaving an infant with other elders who might not understand its early communication attempts so well is a recipe for that infant to shut down those aspects of its brain. Would you choose to do this to your child?

Nurseries can be a good way to shut down your infant's early communication attempts. No well-meaning, well trained nursery worker can substitute for a loving significant elder, particularly a loving attentive mother. If profit is more important than your child, why choose to procreate?

Why have we created a world where profit and economic pressure detracts from the most important task of all? - raising the future, emotionally healthy, intelligent and switched on generations of humanity.

Fortunately, decades of therapy and authentic yoga practice can help remedy this cortisol damage and rebuild healthy and optimally functioning brains and loving hearts.

However, it is so much easier to begin young, isn't it?
Love does matter!

Having come from a warm, dark, pulsing and living womb the transition into brightness, edges and touch is demanding enough without the isolation some babies get. This isolation occurs when the child is put in cots or cribs and left to cry itself to sleep. Babies need to be held close, touched and comforted for at least the first six months. In our world babies are kept close to or on their significant elders for the first six months. Having an earthing celebration where the child is formally laid on the earth in a circle of family and friends is a way to give the child its second birth, from the warm flesh of the family onto the vibrant living earth.

Breastfeeding gives babies liquid love, builds immunity and healthy brains and develops a continued bonding with mother. Mother's milk offers appropriate nutrition and also emotional comfort and is to be encouraged as much as possible. Some women are choosing not to breastfeed so as to not change the shape of their breasts. Some women are choosing to have caesarians instead of vaginal births so as to not change the shape of their vaginas. Vaginal birth fires up bonding neuro-chemicals such as oxytocin and a raft of endorphins that give the next level of bonding after gestation. Obstetric violence in some countries is preventing women from expressing the freedom of choice in how to birth and how to bond with their offspring.

Authentic and appropriate somatic yoga, breath,
meditation, visualisation and relaxation practices build
bonding between mother and the infant inside the womb.
They also strengthen and open the mother's body ready
for a healthy and optimal, even ecstatic birth.

Yes! It is not just okay to feel ecstatic and even orgasmic
during birthing and breastfeeding, it's normal.

We question the psychological development of any man who cannot love a woman whose body has changed after giving birth to his child. If he is so addicted to a particular form that he cannot support the mother of his child as she goes through her profound physical changes and rebuilds her body, what shape is his heart and mind in. Where is the love?

Remember, breasts are primarily mammary glands and offer so much nourishment on every level to a newborn child that it is, (unless there are some medical complications that prevent this) in our opinion close to abusive or neglectful to wilfully withhold that magical nourishment and contact from a newborn child.

Why have a child if you will not give it the love it needs?

The milk bliss a baby feels after breastfeeding as it curls against its mother's body cannot be matched with bottles of formula.

Did you know that the composition of breast milk changes through the day with the evening milk containing components that encourage sleep?

There is evidence that shows that babies regulate their breath through resonance with mother's breath, as long as the mother is not desensitised with alcohol, tobacco or other narcotics. Cot deaths may be more likely for women who isolate their children in cots and cribs.

Avoiding harsh judgements, the ideal scenario for a healthy baby is as natural a birth as possible to a relaxed happy mum who cares for her child with as much touch, holding and breastfeeding as that child needs. An enlightened culture would simply support this process for every mother.

A barbaric, primitive and uncivilised culture would simply put profit and economic power before the wellbeing of mother and child.

The mother's ante-natal preparation and parent's pre-conception preparation would ideally include a few years of asana practice and meditation. For the father, this will help to prepare him to support both mother and children. For the mother somatic practice will help her body be as open as possible for birthing. Breath training will assist the birth process. Deep relaxation, meditation and vibrational work such as mantra can help prepare for the arduous period of sleeplessness and demands that characterise the early stages of the mother and baby relationship.

As a father, I chanted to my children as they rested in their mother's womb, when they came out into the world they knew my voice already. When I sing to them or hold them I am a familiar part of their world, and they can relax even more in my arms. As a man, the most amazing and beautiful thing I have ever seen is the mother of my children giving birth, watching the babies head emerge and then the profound vision of beauty of the mother and baby as the little infant feeds from the breast.

Some old religious yoga texts equate the womb to a pit of slime that each baby grows in. These books were clearly written by unloving and ignorant men.

If we really are to co-create an enlightened society then we need to prioritise attention to care and preparation for mothers and fathers to be, ante-natal care, ecstatic birthing, and consciously tactile and loving parenting.

THE REAL WORLD

Enlightened economics - economics as service

What would an enlightened global economics look and feel like if economics was rooted in service and not greed?

Would we really be trading future commodities and resources, and in so doing push up prices on basic foodstuffs?

Would we really be trading futures so that resource access for our children is likely to be compromised?

If not what would we be doing instead?

What actions can we take now to begin the transformation that is needed?

Would we really have a super wealthy elite divided in almost every way from a hungry, landless and fearful poor?

What might work better for the benefit of all beings?

What is stopping us from co-creating this?

Will we still pretend we could possess, buy and sell strips of the planet's surface?

Will we still be destroying resources and paying no attention to

the future of the planet and its populations of myriad species?

Or, will we be stewarding the land to promote and increase resources and develop mutual harmonious relationships with all the lifeform with which we share this planet?

How might we be doing this?

How might we even begin doing this?

How might we craft our global culture in which contribution to the collective good really is as natural as breathing?

How might we reward such contribution, in whatever way it presents itself, with the means to a healthy and happy quality of life?

Would it be worth measuring the real wealth of nations in quality of life and gross national happiness[11], instead of movements of currency that are, in fact, fabricated?

Real wealth is when the overall balance of financial, personal, collective, social and overarching environmental wellbeing are all taken into consideration. Just having lots of money can make one very, very poor in every other aspect of development as a whole person.

11. Such as in Bhutan where they have four pillars to GNH. They are the promotion of sustainable development, preservation and promotion of cultural values, conservation of the natural environment and establishment of good governance. This is of course simply an example of what could be possible.

*Only a whole person can be really considered
wealthy, others just have lots of stuff.*

*The question that then arises is how do we encourage our
children to be whole and not partial people, shadows desperately
chasing mere currency in a fruitless endeavour to feel safe,
happy and free in the relentless flow of impermanence?*

Money is no longer connected to any real indicators of
wealth anyway. Indicators such as resource or happiness and
wellbeing are divorced from money. Money was detached from
the gold standard many years ago and now we have a currency
that is essentially worthless, yet everyone pretends is valuable.
Not only that, but organisations such as the Federal Reserve,
The International Monetary Fund, The World Bank and The
Bank of England fabricate the amount of money that is flowing around.

When any money is lent to a bank it can then multiply it
by twenty times over in lending despite the fact that it was all
fabricated.

Why can't we fabricate money?

*Why cant we then lend out twenty times that amount to our
friends?*

*How have we agreed that only some people can fabricate currency
and the rest of us cant?*

When such fabrication appears to keep some people in super-

*wealth and others in destitution how can this be considered to be
kind, reasonable, equitable, civilised, or evolved in any way?*

What would an enlightened global economy look like?

It doesn't look like the one we have, that's for sure.

Arguably, real wealth begins with generosity and sharing.
Grasping onto resource is simply one aspect of a pathological
and scared ego.

Let's look at generosity and sharing. Let's begin to see 'super-
wealth' as it is, largely pathological. Anyone who feels they
need vast quantities of money to be happy is probably a little
out of touch with the realities of life. Maybe if such people
practised yoga and meditation, found some authentic inner
peace and contentment, then such pathology would be less
prevalent. Maybe if we all engaged in such somatic and mind
training, found authentic realisation and appreciation for the
flowing and impermanent nature of all phenomenal reality,
then we could relax a little into the flow of life. Relaxed into
the flow of life, there would be less gripping, less possessive
'boundarying' and other such aspects of a fear ridden life.

Finding some authentic realisation of the non-dual, the one
taste of emptiness-form, then we could more easily co-create a
culture, a community of really wise lovingness.

Our belief is that only those free of grasping and attachment
can wisely steward planetary resources for all, this should not
be in the hands of pathological grasping beings. We merely
steward and care for resources for future generations, there is
realistically no possession.

At the risk of repeating, in our view it is better that resources are in the hands of evolved stewards rather than egocentric insecure people who consistently seek identity, security, status, power and control through the illusion of possession and dominance.

What are your feelings and thoughts about this?

How do we know what evolved stewards look and behave like?

How will we become such stewards?

How will we…

develop, integrate and live as an enlightened economy?

• *Realising, seeing and understanding our ego patterns and desires we choose to cultivate, spend and share the wealth that flows through our lives consciously. We will be conscious of what serves both our individual and the collective greater good.*

• *Whilst recognising the conditioning from our parents, families, schools and cultures, we liberate ourselves from all negative conditioning.*

• *We will cultivate positive beliefs, values, attitudes, meanings and behaviours about abundance, wealth and transpersonal[12] development. This will enable us to celebrate abundance for all and serve the greater good.*

• *Let's actively surrender to the abundance and wealth that is this universe and that is our true nature. We will see welcoming and sharing abundance as an act of worship, an act of gratitude and devotion.*

• *Being aware of any old patterns of self-referencing based on possession and the grasping and attachment that drives this behaviour, we let go into real abundance and wealth, surrendering into greater trust and love.*

• *Sustaining generosity, we give freely of the abundance that flows our way. Through generosity we remain in connection with the flow of abundance and life and co-create the flow of abundance for all.*

• *Continuously paying attention to the feedback we receive from the world around us, and from our inner wisdom, we more deeply understand and live the synergy between the greater good of one and all.*

• *We would recognise our transpersonal growth, development and connection to what is as our greatest wealth.*

• *Being conscious, intelligent, wise and aware stewards, we will care for and nourish our personal and collective assets and resources. We all become stewards of planetary resource for the greater good of all.*

• *Awakening into conscious awakened economic relationships, we consistently choose to serve the greater good.*

• *We incorporate this awakening as our body, as our bio-electric-magnetic-field, as our mental awareness, as the richness of our beliefs and behaviours so that we live as this embodied truth. This embodied truth is one of shared abundance as deep love-light, as the source of all, for all.*

• *We know and live the One as the many, the many as the one. We know each in all and all in each. We know this as the way to peace.*

12 People often call this 'spiritual' development. Spiritual as a word is a medieval residue from a dualistic religious worldview that saw two things, creator and creation. From a non-dual perspective the term is largely unhelpful.

The Myth of Freedom?

Freedom can be seen as the freedom from difficult situations and suffering.
This is the freedom from.

Freedom is also the continuous capacity to make clear and informed choices and to act effectively on these.
This is the freedom to.

Freedom is also a state, perhaps best described as a high level of awareness.

Freedom is also a deep experiential knowledge of who and what we are, our core identity.

Freedom can also be experienced and lived as the heart of wisdom. This is the deep, authentic non-dual gnosis of inseparability, absolute as relative, emptiness as form.

Freedom is a multi-faceted experience including the five key aspects of:

• Freedom from constraint

• Freedom to become

• Freedom as awareness

• Freedom of knowing ones deepest identity

• Freedom of the authentically non-dual

Financial wealth without all these components of freedom in place is mere acquisition of resource, just collections of stuff. Whilst currency and resources can be accumulated through unaware states and low level ego-drives, true financial freedom, real wealth can only be attained through fully awakening into who and what we are, and living this reality moment-by-moment, day-by-day.

From realisation we make clear informed choices. With an enlightened economy that serves us, we then act effectively in the world to make these choices and our dreams manifest.

The model below is of our arising from pure Being

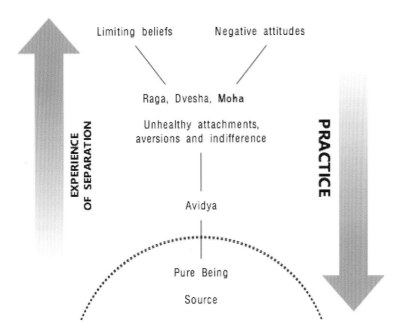

Limiting beliefs   Negative attitudes

Raga, Dvesha, Moha

Unhealthy attachments,
aversions and indifference

Avidya

Pure Being

Source

EXPERIENCE
OF SEPARATION

PRACTICE

of our true nature (avidya or marigpa), as pure-being-ness or source, we can identify and behave as individual limited personalities. It also shows how, through practice and realisation of our true nature, we can remember who we are (vidya or rigpa) and act accordingly. Feeling separate, identified with our sense of separation, we experience a sense of loss, insecurity, and fear.

From this false identity and its perceptual position of a separate self-sense we develop three primary unconscious drives. These three drives are:

• Unhealthy attachment (raga)

• Unhealthy aversion (dvesha)

• Unhealthy and ignorant indifference (moha)

These drives are the natural result of being a separate feeling nervous system. The reflexive responses to these drives lead to temporary feelings of safety or pleasure. These three primary drives manifest through beliefs, values, opinions, thoughts, feelings, muscles, glands, every cell, behaviours, relationships, interpretation of experiences and object creation with our minds. Our life becomes ruled by what Sanskrit calls samsara halahala[13].

Samsara halahala is the reflexive cycles of perception, thought, feeling and behaviour arising from this identity ignorance and its biological consequences.

 Unhealthy attachment and aversion ultimately leads to suffering and dissatisfaction. Since neither these desires nor the objects of these desires will withstand the force of imperma-

13. Literally the poisons of samsara

nence and change there is no safety to be had in such a dynamic. Ultimately neither will our deep innate desire for real connection, the drive for the evolution of consciousness, the deep hunger for truth moving through us be satisfied by such temporary experience.

To top it all, limiting beliefs, negative attitudes and other unhealthy conditioning we have inherited along the way prevents us from accessing real connection to source inside ourselves. This conditioning and its associated patterns of fear also prevent us from recognising 'source' as what it is, total abundance, sublime love, clarity, wisdom, joy and peace.

Moving through the world being dominated by such unhealthy cravings, aversions, ignorance and indifference, all fuelled by our sense of separation, we disengage from the abundant source within us.

We project our past experiences as meanings and beliefs onto the future and through this create cages of limitation for our lives.

Our inability to rest in the present moment is because it feels fragile, insecure and terrifying.

Why? Because to be free, to be source, we have to stop being the self-construct. To stop being the self-construct means the person we have believed we are with all our reference points and feelings of permanence and solidity has to end. The self-construct has to, in a way, 'die'!

The experience of being source is empty of all qualities and reference points except radiant clear awareness, moving as love, joy and wisdom.

To be able to let go and become 'source', we have to feel secure being no one, nothing, and yet finally everything.

Lacking such security in insecurity, we unconsciously keep busy trying to get pleasure and avoid pain in our relationship with the outside world. We do this through grasping at the impermanent play of the elements, building our self-story and using the world as a way of supporting the position (called me) that we fabricate with our minds.

Without awareness, our negative attitudes and limiting beliefs easily misdirect our co-creation. This unconscious blind focus of our life-energies continually manifests a world of unconscious consumption, dissatisfaction and suffering for all of us.

Fortunately, the map above also represents our return to pure Being-ness. By resolving this primary identity ignorance and its native drives of unhealthy attachment, aversion and ignorant indifference we start to wake up and remember who we are.

As we remember who we are, as we awaken from the dream of separation we become this deeper truth of pure being-ness. As we wake up, the tension, suffering and fear associated with our old limiting beliefs and negative attitudes also slowly fades like mist in the morning sun.

To fully resolve this crisis of identity we go to the root and question whom and what we are.

Reflect on the following questions:

Don't expect the answer to be verbal. It will most deeply be a felt experience of clarity at a body-mind-feeling level.

Who am I?

Are we just biological machines moving blindly through gratification and avoidance, attachment and disapproval, craving and aversion, or is there more to our experience and our identity?

What is this life?

What is the truth of this experience?

Is there inherent truth to anything?

Which meanings do I overlay on life as it is?

Is there an inherent purpose to my life or do I get to decide what my purpose is? Is the purpose of life a life of purpose?

What are my beliefs?

Where have these beliefs come from?

Do these beliefs help me?

If I understand that everything really is interconnected and interdependent, if I understand that everything I do, say, think and feel has ramifications and consequences, how do I choose to live my life?

We find that the best questions often generate more questions. Answers that satisfy intellectual, conceptual mind may well be relatively short lived in the light of any deeper more

experiential inquiry and arising insight.

Every time you successfully see and know your ego-desires at the

- *Kinaesthetic level as anxiety or fear sensations and physical holding patterns,*

- *At the emotional level as feelings other than love, compassion, appreciation and joy,*

- *And at the cognitive level as difficult self-talk, critical judgemental thoughts and unskilful beliefs,*

> *...be aware that all these awareness are part of the process, the process of you moving into the greater freedom of pure being, love and authentic freedom.*

In authentic freedom we consciously choose to acquire resources, which we share for the benefit of all. The key words here are benefit and share.

In authentic freedom, rather than the myth of freedom, our desires are aligned with the rich wisdom flow of the cosmos and ultimately serve the greatest good of evolutionary love and wisdom.

Radikal Inquiry

Radikal inquiry is the capacity to continuously and deeply inquire in a consistently gentle but powerful way into every aspect of:

• Nature

• Meaning

• Purpose

• Randomness

• Teachings

• Experience

• Identity

Such radikal inquiry explores paradox, and like zen koans[14] takes us into realisation and comfort with paradox.

Every time you practise, every time you sit, vow to awaken.
Plan to awaken in this practice!
Be utterly present in this moment.
Let this moment be one of real presence

Remember that all feelings other than love, compassion and kindness arise from a lack of correlation. The lack of correla-

tion is between old and dubious internal neurological maps (conditioning) rooted in ignorance of that which we are and the reality of how things really are.

View the reality of what the world is and the reality of
who you are as the realised state of pure-being-ness.

Remember that all feelings other than love arise from toxic conditioning. All behaviours other than love, along with all the strategies of grasping, greed and selfishness arise from the same mistaken view. Realise that love is simply the feeling of clarity or consciousness.

Become equally comfortable with chaos and order, beyond addiction to feelings of connection and without the need for a story of disconnection, know yourself. Realise yourself, in truth, as never not in connection. Realise there is only unicity as diversity.

No longer using every relationship, experience and phenomena to
reference your existence, who are you now?

No longer needing to unconsciously prove you exist and bolster your self-construct with concocted stories and deep meanings, you now know you both exist and to not exist.

Now, can you relax, laughing, into this beautiful paradox?

When we fully realise our abundant existence we no longer need to grasp for abundance, we are this flow.

Re-cognising[15] we are intimate connection, we are relational beings, we are the interdependent web of life. Yet, we are also

---

14. Koans are puzzles offered by a teacher to a student. The puzzles cannot be understood or answered rationally. It is only insight that can resolve the paradox of koan.

15. Literally re-knowing or remembering!

the unique and individual, conventional experience of permeable and fractal boundary that we laughingly call 'Me' and 'You'.

Realising our deepest nature as empty, radiant Being-ness whilst also being the transient flow of impermanence, one infinite play of paradox.

Sustaining this awareness, we continuously rest, effortlessly as this.

The wise discrimination, the native intelligence of love now allows us to know in every moment what choices serve life in its deeper flow.

Use this day wisely, enjoy and deepen in radikal inquiry.

Real assets are wealth...

What's an asset?

Assets can be seen as the resources that facilitate and positively contribute to our experience of life.

Material assets include:

• Practical resources such as food, shelter and clean drinking water

• Money - simply, as the current global means of resource exchange

• Real wealth as free flowing generosity

• Stewardship of planetary resource

Physical assets include:

• Radiant wellbeing

• Strength

• Flexibility and openness

• Fitness - cardio, structural, fascial, digestive and neurological

• Good immune system and organ function

• Somatic intelligence

Emotional assets include:

• Emotional literacy - knowing what your emotions are, distinguishing one from another

• Emotional intelligence - understanding your emotions as an aspect of body intelligence and what they are communicating

• Appropriate personal management of emotional states - choices that lead to freedom and the co-creation of mutual loving relationships

• Clear flowing emotions free of conditioned stagnation, taboos, repression or suppression

• Emotional freedom - resolution of dualistically distorted flows of the feeling world that then reveal the inseparability

• Non-contextual joy as a base line operating system

Cognitive assets include:

• Positive belief

• Cherished values

• Faith based on direct experience

• Consistent inquiry

• Non-attachment to viewpoints, whilst respecting the multiplicity of possible viewpoints, 'darshanas', and the role of these

• Clear thinking and rationality

• Wise discrimination that serves the greater good

• Wisdom and love in everyday action

Transpersonal developmental (spiritual) assets include:
• Luminous vast awareness

• A lived realisation of emptiness

• A lived realisation of connection and inter-dependence

• Real self-knowledge

• Devotion to teachers, teachings and more

• Deeply lived bio-philia

• Unobstructed love as appreciation, kindness, compassion and more

• Living wisdom as the direct perceptual clarity of the nature of reality

• Resolution of the self-construct into transparency and radiance

• Service to conscious evolution and humanity as the work of freedom

This investigation into assets is intended to promote your own inquiry, to encourage the beginning of a vast work of dedication to co-create a globally enlightened, compassionate and wise economy.

We have to begin somewhere, don't we?

Generosity

Let us remember that from the yogic view, the interpretation of prosperity as 'possessing' is a fearful and marginal prosperity, more mere grasping. Real wealth is the capacity to be in 'flow'.

In 'flow' one is fully open to receive wealth and abundance from life's infinite generosity, which is then mirrored by one's capacity to give. After all, we are that generosity, that universal flow.

Detachment is often presented as a 'spiritual' ideal. Yet detachment isn't flow, detachment is occupying a space apart from this which seeks to control and not 'go with the flow'!

If one struggles with this perspective of flow, then the practice of generosity is a necessary antidote and preliminary preparation for deeper yogic practice.

From the direct experience of being both giver and receiver in flow comes the realisation of the universe as sublimely abundant.

Hence the highly revered and important place given to 'Dana' or generosity in transpersonal development and 'conscious evolutionary' traditions such as yoga and Buddhism.

In our modern technologically advanced and supposedly civilised world, 3% of the planetary population own and control 90% of the planetary resources. This tragedy is compounded by the simple fact that there is more than enough resource to go around. If it were a matter of quantity of resource alone, we could feed, clothe and house everyone and provide all basic human needs.

As Mahatma Gandhi said:
"The earth provides enough for every man's need but not for every man's greed"

Yet, half of our planetary population go hungry and thirsty every day. Millions of human beings die from lack of food, clean water and simple healthcare.

What in actual fact belongs to us?

The essential teachings of Buddhism and Yoga include the potent message of the complete and endlessly dependent arising and inter-dependence of all things. This is the recognition of all phenomena (material, sensory, emotional, and intellectual) as aspects of a complex web of interconnectivity extending through time and space.

When we understand our existence as being inextricably linked to everything else how, realistically, can the idea of something being 'mine' make any sense?

Who is this person who has the territory of 'mine'?

Surely our feelings depend on our upbringing and how we have learned, chosen and grown into relationship with ourselves and with others. Our thoughts depend on what we read or see, our schooling, and the influences in our life. Our breath is dependent on plants that are themselves dependent on sunlight, soil, and water. Plants also depend on insects for their reproduction, and on all creatures for their exhaled carbon dioxide. Plants are the primary producers of all food on this planet. It is on plants that

we rely for the creation of our own lifeform and existence.
All things are composed of the myriad parts of other things.
In origin, all of it is star-stuff spinning in space. Star-stuff
in its entirety, all of matter is simply dancing, whirling
energy, and so the inter-dependence of all things flows.
As our contemporary science of ecology teaches us, we are
never not in connection, never not interdependent, never not
in relationship, throughout the past, present, and future.

Compassionate and integral spiritual teachings understand the absolute and conventional (or relative) perspectives, as inseparable and non-dual. This great equation of the non-dual is therefore simple. The miraculous and complex flow of inter-dependence and the ground of being, the quantum field, the matrix and ground of all existence really are one inseparable unicity.

In accordance with Indian Tantric view, the changing flow of nature (as viewed from our sensory systems) is understood as the 'feminine'. The quantum field, the ground of being or the 'Ubgrund' is understood as the 'masculine'. The Tibetan Tantric view has the poles reversed with the emptiness of the Ubgrund as feminine and the flow of phenomena or form as the masculine.

Both poles, as one, create the totality of what is. This is like the Yin balancing and supporting the Yang and vice versa. This relative and changing realm of inter-dependence is then a celebration of the ineffable absolute in its eternal dance. We are part of the play of subject and object, being both the absolute and the relative, both as one non-dual reality, right here, right now!

The beauty of yogic method is that none of this needs to be 'true'. We don't need another dogma. However, if we act as if this were true and it yields the results of realisation, then the living truth of realisation moves as greater life, rather than the corpses of dogma making life smaller and more fearful.

Biophilic (life-loving) spiritual teachings honour and celebrate incarnation as special, wonderful and beautiful. These teachings view changing and relative nature as a profoundly fertile space to explore, understand, develop and engage in kindness-compassion-love and intelligence-wisdom, and to deeply enjoy life.

Rather than being interested in a fool's 'liberation' that gets us 'out of here' as quickly as possible, incarnation becomes a powerful possibility to really know inter-dependence. Knowing connection through incarnation, whilst also knowing existence as the absolute, invites us to fully explore love, compassion and kindness. It is the vulnerability and fragility of impermanence that brings home the reality of our situation.

Now, love is beginning to be expressed through generosity. Generosity is really the beginning and the fulfilment of love.

The authentic spontaneous giving of resources and service
is a way we connect with, contribute to, and celebrate
the flow of abundance and prosperity. Connection is a
process of being compassionately present, of awareness
as immanence in abundance. It is through immanence
that the experience of transcendence arises.

Many religious traditions promote giving as a fundamental tenet of their more positive belief structures. Christians and Muslims were exhorted to give one tenth of their net profit to charitable works. Under the laws of these religions it was, until the advent of contemporary capitalism, illegal to make money through interest on money lent. This is also a kind and greed free way of doing business. The founder of the Sikh religion Guru Nanak included the practice of Dana (charitable and generous giving) and Seva (service) as the prime responsibilities of any follower seeking to lead a righteous life. The tenth century Sanskrit text, the Bhagavata Purana, celebrating the yoga of devotion includes the Ashtanga system as codified by the great sage Patanjali. In contrast to Patanjali however, its author Vyasa adds in five more yamas (practices of moral discipline) and five more niyamas (practices of self-restraint). One of these additional niyamas is Dana.

In the Chandogya Upanishad, the Vedic work in which the Gayatri mantra is expounded, we find Dana spoken of as a sacrificial gift. Giving to other beings is giving to the divinity, to the totality, to the source and sum of all. The Chandogya recognises a life that includes Dana as the best recompense for the priceless gifts of love received from one's teachers.

We, as infinite source[16], give a gift (which is also infinite source) to a recipient (who is infinite source). Source is also giver, giving, gift, and receiver.

Is the one who receives giving the gift of generosity to the giver?

Isn't giving and receiving the experience of connection, unicity as multiplicity?

Such generosity and simple humanism was considered by Haribhadra Suri in his Jaina text, Yoga-Bindu from 750 (C.E.) as an essential preparation for the practices of yoga.

Buddhists are encouraged to give Dana as a primary aspect of their religious practice. Before beginning any of the ten perfections, before even engaging in ethics comes Dana. This generosity of Spirit culminates in the ideal of the Mahayana tradition, the Bodhisattva.

Bodhisattvas are Beings who are dedicated to the evolutionary and developmental awakening of all Beings, themselves and others alike. Bodhisattvas make every effort to understand, experience and attain their own complete awakening so that they can more effectively serve others.

What a gift to see that it is our responsibility to welcome prosperity and wealth so that we can give more, give fully, and give freely?

Generously giving one tenth of your net profit could be the best investment you ever make. Doing this intimately connects you with flow. Supporter, supporting, support and supported. Giver, giving, gift and receiver. Love, loving, lover and beloved. All are interconnected, interdependent and unified as the flow of the totality, the One as the many, the many as the One. An attitude of gratitude for everything as it is, for this perfect moment in flow is a powerful foundation from which to cultivate growth.

16. This is not some sort of endless ketchup, but the beginningless and endless emptiness which is the pregnant possibility and flow of life and form.

Cultivating non-contextual gratitude, satisfaction and joy with every arising phenomenon in every moment is the yogic practice of Santosha. This can lead to such levels of contentment and equanimity that joy becomes the foundation of experience. Santosha is a totally different experience to conventional joy. Conventional joy is simply a peak of neurochemical production that is completely dependent on external factors for it's arising and delimited by the ever-present tensions of fear and loss.

Santosha is one of the key preparatory practices of the Ashtanga Yoga system, a practice that finally makes sense upon full awakening.

Yet in vowing to practice Santosha, and failing, we get to see our neurotic strategies of craving, aversion and ignorant indifference. Through the continual arising awareness of unhelpful patterns our bad habits of selfishness are revealed. These strategies become utterly transparent to the clear vast awareness that we really are, underneath all the patterns of contraction and fear.

Moments of clarity with the concomitant feeling of love are actually moments of not doing fear, not doing contraction. These moments can slowly unite and coalesce into a flowing stream of openness to our beginning-less nature.

As this process unfolds, we step into the unknown with courage, joy and gratitude. Curiosity and playfulness now expand as we enjoy diving into the shadowy depths and flying to the luminous heights within.

Gradually become free of the old obstacles, the unconscious limiting patterns of thought and feeling. Endeavour to achieve this whilst sustaining the power and vitality derived from practice and the purpose that has no other purpose than this co-creative moment of presence that is.

This deeper identity of vast awareness with its infinite levels of possibility, allow us to begin richly expressing the innate genius, creativity and essence that we are. From this space of creative genius, we manifest our desires and needs in a way that fully respects this newfound identity, an identity in respectful union and inter-dependence.

Co-creating new worlds together, expressing our deep creative freedoms and sharing from a place of generosity of heart allows each of us to access the natural abundance and prosperity of infinite source, which has always been our original nature.

Politics as Service

Zero Tolerance

Why do we tolerate politicians who lack integrity?

Contemporary culture repeatedly evidences political leaders in dubious alliance with corporate leaders and corporate leaders who evidence little ecological or social concern.

But can we help them grow when they wrap themselves in layer upon layer of legislation, military and police protection, and display relentless strategies of manipulation, deceit, denial and defensiveness.

How can we help them find a more aware life?

Of course there are exemplary and benevolent leaders of business, there are politicians of integrity too. We welcome all business leaders and politicians of integrity to join us, stand up and be counted.

Perhaps politicians who do not exhibit ecological intelligence are not worthy of being facilitated by our votes, money, or support?

Perhaps politicians who promote policies lacking in compassion and recognition of inseparability are not deserving of being facilitated by our votes, money, or support?

Is it not time we had a global alliance of nations with wise and awakened leadership? Leaders entirely accountable to their constituency and who are in service to the collective greater good rather than personal gain are absolutely essential.

How will we get this or something even better to grow?

Stewardship of this planet and its resources leads to mutual wellbeing, abundance, prosperity, and peace for all people and all species. Anything short of this and we are selling our planet, our children and our grandchildren short.

We know that ultimately the whole planet will burn up as the sun explodes. Until this deadline is reached then stewardship, appreciation and love for this blue jewel of a planet is a wise way forward.

How are we going to co-create awakened planetary governance which honours the ecological web and really works to limit the damage our species creates whilst seeking to generate wellbeing for all?

We look forward to this being in place. We look forward to the work of the transition that is already in process.

We invite your feedback and collaboration in creating a world where those who go into politics do so as a form of service to the greater good. We welcome a world where those who stand up as leaders can be counted upon as having courage and integrity and standing for what is true.

What are your thoughts?

CONSCIOUS CULTURE

Conscious culture co-creation

Firstly, it's good to recognise that we continuously co-create culture. Culture is the collective framework in which we help incubate and mature our future generations. Usually, culture is co-created unconsciously.

Culture is always based on what came before, there are many elements of 'it was always done like that so it has to continue'... Does it?

In what ways can we rethink everything?

How do we work out exactly what is valuable from the past and what to drop?

What no longer serves us?

Our culture is relatively recently post-feudal. In the UK we still have feudal overlords and clergy in government, and a feudal monarchy as head of state. Feudal monarchs had to be pathological simply to survive and breed. They had to be ready to torture, impale, behead, crucify, slaughter, commit genocide or whatever was perceived necessary to sustain their lineage, their nation and their wealth.

In sublimated form, these qualities have moved across to the business world. Here, psychological testing indicates that we still tend to unconsciously (or consciously) select for these qualities amongst business leaders and politicians.

Most people still revere such feudal characteristics as representative of greatness, we, however, don't.

One of the fantastic qualities we human beings share is our ability to abstract. Abstraction in this sense is taking ourselves out of a situation, separating ourselves from it, and imagining a completely different scenario than the one we currently occupy. This creative capacity allows for planning the future, crafting great art works and co-creating enlightened cultures.

When this awesomely creative capacity is mobilised through a sense-of-self (ego), which has an un-evolved emotional intelligence, the result is either dissociated fantasy or ugly barbarity.

The capacity to separate away from others and treat them with contempt and barbarity is the result of such pathological dissociation. Pathological dissociation is the shadow side of the potential of creative abstraction. Creative abstraction leads to great art, great music, great literature, and real civilisation. Creative abstraction leads people to treat their lives as if they were art. We revere and celebrate awesome creativity. Isn't it interesting that pathological dissociation and creativity are opposite poles of the same energy.

How do we move from pathology to beauty as a culture?

We currently create computer games, some of which entrain our younger generations in grotesque (virtual) behaviours such as robbery, murder and illicit activities.

Is this intelligent culture creation?

Our childcare practices do not always serve to create the most emotionally intelligent brains, they do not always help to bring out the greatest potential in each of us.

When childcare is given such a low cultural priority, is this surprising?

People prioritise making money and profit over childcare, is this really an intelligent evolutionary strategy?

What are we to do about it?

We recommend Sue Gerhardt's work as a starter on this topic. Her first book Why Love Matters explores creating emotionally intelligent brains, and her second book Selfish Society looks at how to create a culture of selfishness and indifference. If we want a culture of selfishness then we co-create a culture where brain development leads to emotional dysfunction and feelings of separation and disconnection. Is such a culture in any way sustainable? Probably not.

Seeing some of the problems is a beginning, now…

What do we choose to co-create?

Are we not, each of us, responsible for our own circle of influence?

A potent belief is that everyone ultimately wants love, tolerance and respect.

How might we choose to embrace and foster these natural rights and qualities, and more, within our culture?

How do we choose to educate our population about our own minds, our own emotional responses, and take responsibility for our own wellbeing and our creative power?

Consequently, how do we choose to build a world that is more clearly based on mutual love, respect and vibrant creativity?

From Mind, through architecture, into the future…

Chris was standing outside the Buddhist centre in Newcastle in the UK before teaching a workshop. He was chatting to a bright young man and their conversation turned to the subject of culture creation.

The architecture was grim. Vast red brick walls, sharp edges, metal bars, grey tarmac, a soul-less and barren urban landscape.

Chris asked "Did you design this?"

The young man said "No"

Chris said "Neither did I. What would it look like if you did?"

All of our world has come out of mind. Everything arises out of imagination and moves through mind into form. Where do the minds that had the vision for and those that crafted this brutal urban landscape arise from?

We know people suffer from 'sick building syndrome'. This is where architecture dysfunctionally affects people's state of mind. People used to build with respect to the ratios of perspective found in nature[17], people used to build in relation to the contours of the earth. Now we are living with the psychological and emotional consequences of the architecture legacies of the last half century.

If we look at the world around us and contemplate how and why it is as it is, would we reproduce it that way or would we do something different?

This is an important question because if we understand the consequences of cultural conditioning in terms of culture creation then we can begin to co-create something positively different.

The essence of this book is to invite us to deconstruct everything and re-think everything. Let's co-create[18] our culture and world from a place of bright creativity that really honours the holotropic[19] perspective that recognises the inseparable nature of reality.

We recognise that many people revere the psychopathic men who inhabit our history books. Many people love to construct and admire memorials to them, and to the wars that have been the highlight of so many of our social myths.

There is a statue on a side street near the river Rhine in Dusseldorf, Germany, of a mother and child. The statue is a poetic and evocative celebration of love.

Why are there not more statues like this and less of the pompous generals on their war horses?'

Why do we choose to celebrate the atrocities of war and destruction in preference to celebrating love and simple humanity?

Has mother love ever been publicly revered as much as the capacity to commit genocide in the name of some superior race or another?

So when we explore how we co-create culture and become conscious about it, what shape will our future have?

Will it be the world according to gruesome apocalyptic Hollywood

---

17. The golden ratio Phi and the Fibonacci sequence.

18. Co-create means together in mutual relationship! This relating has both systemic and integral qualities. Systemic is the interwoven web of ecology. Integral is the interwoven web of emptiness as form, form as emptiness.

19. Holotropic means moving towards wholeness.

fantasies, patriarchal Abrahamaic prophesies or will it be something different?

Do you have any influence?

Do you have any power to co-create?

What do you choose?

Initiation

For the first time in the history of the human species (with a few exceptions) we are living much longer lives. With the expectation for most contemporary western people of living until their mid seventies, or even much older, age and all it brings is a novel experience to the relatively recently evolved Homo sapiens.

What does age bring?

There are many cultural mythologies of ageing, many of them quite negative, and in the western world elders are often segregated from younger folk in institutional settings.

What is the reality of ageing and what is truly possible in terms of remaining in vibrant wellbeing?

What is the most enlightened way we can celebrate ageing whilst sustaining high quality lives and remaining vibrant and valued members of our culture, rather than being isolated in some cultural divide and being viewed, quite often, as irrelevant?

How do we choose to manage the process of death?

Again, the modern western tendency is to clinically isolate death in a 'photoshopped' culture that mostly seeks to keep dying hygienic and out of sight, and therefore out of mind. Anyone who has been to the ancient city of Benares will know that some cultures openly accept and even celebrate death in ways that are utterly shocking to modern westerners. One thing is sure, I'm going to die, you are going to die, everyone will die, eventually…

How do we choose to celebrate death in our brave new world?

In the western world we have a historical tendency to build mausoleums and tombs, covering acres of ground in an endeavour to carry the memory of someone's life into the future. What is the best way that we can honour the process of death, be open to it, and allow memories to be honoured whilst no longer deluding ourselves about the ever-present reality of death?

Young women have natural processes of initiation. These processes of menarche, monthly menstruation, pregnancy, childbirth, and menopause potentially mark the transitions of a young woman's life through to maturity. The masculist culture and its tendency to fear all these processes relegates them to being ignored, pilloried as unclean, or medicalised as problems.

Menstruation in older cultures would have been relatively less evident, in as much as many women spent several years either pregnant or in lactational amenorhea. Despite that, many cultures have labelled this process unclean and teach their young women to resent or despise it, or to feel shamed by it.

The 'curse', as it has been called, has been thought of very differently in older Tantric cultures, for example. It was called 'Flowers of the holy well' - *Kundapuspa* or *Yonipuspa* in such world-views. The Yoni is the generic term for the vagina,

womb and the creative fount of the whole cosmos, the whole play of space-time. In more women-friendly, womb-friendly cultures menstruation has been honoured as the powerful, magical force of fertility and creativity that it is. Slowly, more of us may be returning to this recognition.

We may also be heading towards an alarmingly medicalised menstruation process where implants transform physiology (see the work of Dr Elsimir Coutinho) and women can leap around in white clothes just like sanitary towel advertisements.

What do you choose? Ecological connection or chemically moderated disconnection?

The powerful initiation of conscious menstruation which links women inexorably to the earth, to the tides and the moon, to the cycles of life, time and space - though ignored by the masculist western world - could be the way for women to deeply connect to our mothership, to the planet itself. Men could deeply honour this process and facilitate space for women to deepen in mutual relationship. Since men do not have the psycho-physiological power that conscious-menstruation can offer, they too could choose to appreciate blood times as ovulation times and become involved in this mutual dance of honouring as a part of their own work towards freedom.

Conscious menopause is also a time of individual and cultural initiation into the role of the crone.

The empire cultures of the world have always flourished through divide and rule. If women are divided against each other in competition for men, divided young against old, and their creative power and life energies sapped in a relentless en-

deavour to fit into the latest fashion items or to get their bodies to fit the latest trends of what physical shape is perceived as valuable, then more than 50% of humanity are disempowered.

Conscious menopause could involve initiation into the status of being an elder, of being the ones that remember, of teaching the younger ones. Segregating the past and the lessons of history means we are most likely doomed to repeat them again and again.

How will we choose to honour our elders?

Traditionally men would have been initiated into their role and the responsibility of being a man within their culture.

What does manhood mean? How is it different to being a boy?

Today, the initiation of men, if it occurs at all, seems to be courtesy of pornographers, narcotics provided through criminal organisations, street violence and licentious sex.

Does this teach young men the roles and responsibilities of being a responsible and responsive adult?

Does the 'lad' culture of 'the one who has the most 'toys' wins' serve the role of facilitating responsibility for the upcoming generation, for the planet and for the future? Probably not.

With the media spotlight on politicians helping themselves to public funds, bankers helping themselves to vast bonuses, spiritual leaders and celebrities having abused their positions of trust by sexually abusing youngsters, what faith can be had in male elders?

Where are the authentic male elders?

Are elders as a cultural phenomena, both female and male, a thing of the past? Are our elders only celebrated for their contributions and achievements after their deaths?

Is it that now all people are simply consumers, trying to get their piece of the pie?

In our growing and consciously evolving culture, what is the role of initiation?

What is the role of consciously celebrating the life changes that each of us goes through?

What is the best way to honour each other, men and women, and co-create an enlightened world?

Collective decision-making

Once upon a time, all decisions were made by the noblesse oblige. These were (and still are) the pathological few who believed they had the 'divine right' to rule over those whose destiny it was to be serfs. The overlords of both state and religion were in clear allegiance, and anybody who disagreed with their dictates was brutally punished.

Since then we have evolved to a slightly more democratic model of some accountability where some of the population vote[20] for one of two or more 'agenda-driven' groups of people, who are supposed to represent the electorates viewpoints and desires. The reality is still that the groups who can vie for power are funded by vast quantities of money. They have to be backed by big money or they would not be able to stand.

The reality is that a pseudo-accountability exists but is quite opaque at times, as we keep seeing with the corruption evident in politicians, globally. The relentless appearance of politicians lining their own pockets as they kowtow to big business is becoming rather jaded for the ordinary man and woman struggling to pay the rent or mortgage and feed and educate their children.

The reality appears to be a charade, that the only power the electorate really have is to put a mark on a piece of paper every few years or so and then stand in the streets and protest if they don't like what their elected 'representatives' are doing.

Their elected representatives may then also turn the full brutality of the forces of law and order on them for their vocal inquiry and prohibit such public inquiry into the issues being explored.

To date, this is how we have collectively chosen to make decisions.

And even this is rare! Across most of the world such liberty is still a long way off. Many people still live in regimes where religious dictators, secular dictators, power groups or other forms of dictatorial control still dominate political process.

Is this really the best we can do as an intelligent, informed species?

In some contemporary groups of people seeking an evolutionary decision-making process the focus is on consensus. Consensus is where issues are discussed over time and the whole group come to an agreement about the best way forward.

This is a fantastic idea and certainly has more collective involvement than the divine right, dictatorial or democratic models of decision-making.

One aspect of consensus that can become problematic is the issue of gripping onto views. If one person in the group is stubbornly insistent on their viewpoint and can hang on interminably then the whole process can be undermined. In contrast to those who dominate groups are those who rest relatively uninvolved, both strategies sabotage the authenticity of consensus.

One means to resolve this is to co-create a culture of participation and consensus where a feeling of common ground is sought. We always have common ground. We all need food, shelter, water and good relationships within and outside our community. When we recognise this common ground is what

20. On average 60% in both the UK and USA

we are all seeking, then we can arrive at a decision where the result of which will serve the greater good. This approach transcends the preoccupation with merely advancing our personal opinions or agenda.

A culture of participation is facilitated when people are valued for their contribution, and each contribution is seen as a gift to the group, a gift that will assist the synergy of problem solving.

There is evidence that in decision-circles the collective intelligence of the group comes into play. Collective intelligence is a synergy where solutions to problems are more easily and more fully found. The right attitude of seeking common ground and participation has to be present for this to work effectively. This balances the more competitive and challenging energies we humans do so well with appreciative participation.

We test ran another model of community decision making which worked well. Like any model it has its weaknesses too, and areas that could do well with being ironed out. See if you can spot these weaknesses.

Decisions fall into different levels of gravity. There are always smaller, less influential decisions and larger, more complex issues to sort out in any community.

Having five different levels of decision complexity is one approach.

For example, we might have simpler level-one decisions, such as how do we decide who does the washing up, shopping or cooking?

A level-four decision has much greater complexity, such as which new property do we buy and why?

A different consensus time-frame is attributed to each level of decision.

This means that with the culture of consensus in place the aim for the group was to find a solution to the problem within that time frame.

The time frame was expansive enough to allow deep discussion of all the issues involved and included several sittings to explore all the issues.

Another aspect of this puzzle was to seek and share as much information as possible allowing informed, evidence based, decision making.

The time-frame concept, consensus culture, information rich process and seeking common ground encourage finding decisions that work for the whole community.

If the time frame was transcended without consensus being reached then the decision process devolved to the democratic model and a majority vote was taken and followed.

What are some of the issues with this process?

Well, first, who decides which issue fits into which decision level?

Second, if vested groups of interest still choose to they can extend the discussion to go beyond the consensus frame and push to get a majority vote that they feel they can win.

So we have to work with culture creation as the pre-requisite for any enlightened decision-making process.

Can you come up with better models?
Share them please.

JOBS /EMPLOYMENT.

Out of question - feeling Bristolian
nies sometimes difficult to reach
eng at the bottom of the Pile

Yoga is ultimately about co-creating an awakened planet.

As Engaged Yoga practitioners we have to look at these areas of human process so we can bring the light of love, wisdom and responsible freedom to all our relational experiences.

We learn to love by being mutually involved.

Breathing Breaks

*Take breathing breaks at least four times a day, go
on, take nine full deep breaths each time.*

Simple micro-practices like this keep the central nervous system (CNS) in relaxation mode as much as possible, and allow a more loving perspective on life.

Many people have stressful jobs, busy lives, and relentless demands for their time, attention, and money. Taking responsibility for one's own CNS and keeping it as relaxed and responsive[21] as possible is a good counterpoint to the relentless 'adrenalised' demands of contemporary life.

Stress is known to contribute to all the major killers including the cardio-vascular diseases (strokes and heart attacks), diabetes, and cancer. Stress is implicated in many other conditions from eczema to asthma, headaches to heartburn and arthritis to early onset conditions of ageing. Stress is a killer and can destroy the quality of your life and the lives of those around you.

Having tools like Yogic Trancework, Power Nidra and meditation in our toolbox we can then cultivate a nervous system that rests more easily in (what Herbert Benson called) the Relaxation Response, rather than living in (what Hans Selye called) the Stress Response, or the Physical Emergency Response.

Breath based practices like the Ujjayi breath, which can be practised anywhere, allow us to nourish and care for our CNS and reduce the damage caused by stress and the demands of contemporary living, wherever we are, whatever we are doing.

21. rather than reactive…

All of life is an opportunity for practice and realisation.

When each one of us takes responsibility for our own thinking, our own feelings, our own behaviour, and all the consequences of these, we have a conscious culture.

The antithesis of such a world is a culture of shame and blame. When we blame everyone else for our reality and refuse to take responsibility then we have a culture of blame. You can read cheap tabloid newspapers and feel the culture of blame.

*Now, choose to take responsibility. Blame puts you in the
place of the victim, whilst responsibility is empowering.*

Taking control of our own CNS and enabling internal creative space, between stimulus and response, is the way of choice, consciousness and responsibility.

Living from a place of reflexive patterning, unconsciousness, and minimal choice is the way of disempowerment.

*To create a conscious culture we have to be conscious. A
culture is made of individuals. If the individuals are less
than conscious, living in reflexive patterns, disempowered
and blaming then that is the essence of the culture.*

*If the individuals within the culture are taking responsibility
for their own CNS, their thinking, their feelings,
their behaviour, and living from a place of spacious
creativity then that is the essence of the culture.*

Breath, along with a good somatic practice, is the most rapid route to work directly with one's own CNS. This needs to be followed with meditative practice and all the other facets of an

integral yogic practice. Integral and engaged practices allow an authentic resolution for the conditioned reflexes of existence.

A conscious culture is, in essence, a yogic culture in its broadest sense.

Take regular breathing breaks.

Relaxation and Re-creation

Recreation is important! The capacity and the opportunity to relax into life is crucial to wellbeing, continued creativity, and real enjoyment.

Recreation that is sensitive enough to the lives of other people and members of other species is switching on to an enlightened process.

How are you going to relax and re-create?
Play music?
Dance?
Sit by the ocean?
Surf?
Walk in the woods and mountains?
Practice parkour?
Climb?
Run?
Drive ecologically destructive internal combustion engines at furious speed?

Part of a quality lifestyle of weaving yoga into everyday life is to facilitate relaxation and recreation for all. The balance of the sympathetic and parasympathetic nervous systems is crucial for wellbeing, it is crucial for creativity. Our culture is dependent on creativity; creativity is enhanced by appropriate amounts of relaxation. Great inventions often occur in daydreams:

Kekule discovered the benzene ring[22] after dreaming of a snake eating its own tail, just like the great mythic serpent Ouroboros. Ouroboros represents infinity, the eternal cycle of life, death, time and space as well as the movement of the sun.

Einstein discovered the principle of relativity after dreaming of riding on a sunbeam.

Crick and Watson apparently discovered the alpha helix shape for DNA after dreaming of two snakes spiralling around each other.

Samuel Taylor Coleridge composed one of his romantic epics titled Kubla Khan after an opium inspired dream.

Sir Paul McCartney dreamed up the melody for the beautiful song 'Yesterday', which contains the lyrics "When all my troubles seemed so far away, yes I believe in…"

President Abraham Lincoln dreamed of his death a few days prior to the event. It is tradition in some indigenous cultures for the elders to dream of the time of their death and to then walk out into the wilderness to meet their death, at peace and alone.

Some mathematicians, including the great Ramanujan, dreamt up works inspired by a muse, or as is said in Ramanujan's case, a feminine deity.

Chuang-Tzu[23] dreamed of being a butterfly dreaming it was a human being dreaming of being a butterfly… So arose much contemplation on the nature of mind and meaning.

How much more art, science, and philosophy is inspired by daydreams?
What do your daydreams inspire you to do or be?

How will you allow recreation to be your platform from which to co-create?

22. The benzene ring is the chemical structure of benzene discovered by the German chemist August Kekule.

23. Chuang-Tzu was a fourth century (CE) Taoist philosopher from China.

A conscious culture is one in which creativity plays a large part and which celebrates and creates space and time for relaxation, recreation and creativity. The suppression of creativity to drive an unsustainable and economically unsound culture serves no one.

Before going to sleep

Consider your day.

What happened?

How did you respond to what happened?

What would you have done differently?

What would you have done the same?

What have you learned about love, life and your self?

What golden moments were there to totally celebrate?

How will you cherish them?

*Now, tune into your breath, let go of the day
and study your dominant hand.*

*Study your hand well and decide to wake up in your
dreams. When waking up in your dreams play freely and
then choose to look at the mind that is dreaming.*

*Choose to rest well, dream lucidly and well, and to
wake up feeling refreshed, rejuvenated and ready
for the next day of creative empowerment.*

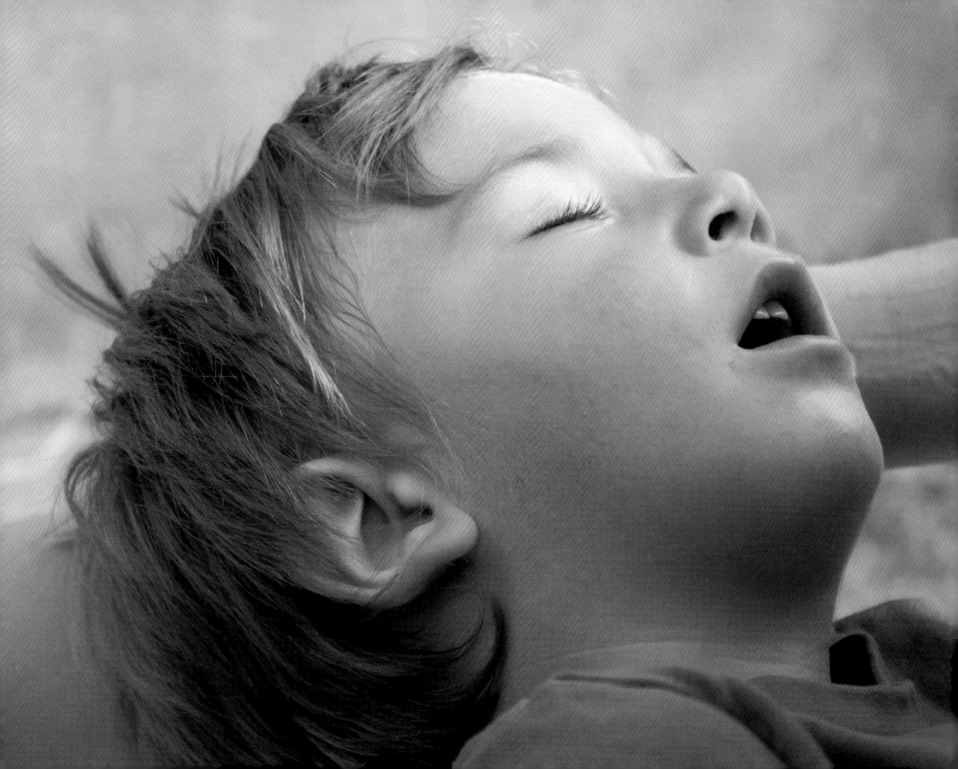

CONSCIOUS EVOLUTION

Yoga as Conscious Evolution

Our current premise is that, throughout evolution, there is a consistent multi-faceted theme occurring. This theme is one of overall growth into greater, more expansive and more Self-reflective consciousness. As Engaged Yoga practitioners we acknowledge and work with this flow.

This section on yoga as conscious evolution is offering a dogma-free view that is an exploration and an invitation for us to deepen in our exploration, our inquiry, and our community.

Really, evolution is a process of co-evolution. Evolution is a function of inter-dependence and impermanence, nothing evolves alone.

A flowering plant can only evolve along with a pollinating insect. Both flower and insect are in the process of interdependent co-evolution. All of life is in the process of interdependent co-evolution.

Organisms are not separate from their environment. The flow of water, minerals and atmospheric gases are also what that organism is. Changes in the environment are what influence an organism's survival. As environmental conditions change, and they do, then the genetic material that offers an advantage in those changed conditions will be selected for.

We humans dramatically change our environment; we are already deeply engaged in unconscious evolution as we transform our world around us. We are now in the geological age called the Anthropocene. This is the age where the main factor affecting ecological change is the human species. As we affect our environment we affect which genes are selected for.

We could, of course, make our environment so hostile that only cockroaches and Cyborgs could survive! We could also pay attention to the thirteen key-points of conscious evolution and start to work with co-creative, conscious co-evolution.

What choice will we make?

We consider the following thirteen key-points extremely worthy of attention, there may well be others. These thirteen key-points are intended to help us as practitioners, and as a species, pay attention to our place in the flow of evolution and how we consciously work with this flow.

If we consciously work with this flow maybe we will practice yoga as conscious evolution. Yoga has always offered assistance in aligning with the force of conscious evolution, bringing mindfulness into all aspects of daily life.

The supreme state of mindfulness is super-consciousness. This is where one is both mindful and heart-fully aware of the ripples in space-time that are the consequence of every word, deed and action. Buddha Maitreya is taught to be the future Buddha. Buddha simply means 'awakened one' and Maitreya means 'friend of all'. We understand the 'Maitreya principle' to be a metaphor for the time in human evolution when we all understand inseparability, and therefore treat each other with love, respect, tolerance, and simple kindness. We are all Maitreya.

Similarly, Vedic[24] teaching has always been that we are all Brahman, that everything is Brahman. Brahman is the totality, the inseparability, the absolute and the relative flow, the many

---

24. One of the core (arguably the main) philosophical systems of India.

and the One, the One as the many and the many as the One.

When we realise, when we see, feel and live as Brahman, the only result is kindness to all, friendliness to all, respect to all, and love as and for all.

Maitreya is another representation, another metaphor for this level of realisation.

We are a long way off this level of evolved consciousness. Engaged Yoga where yoga is understood as conscious evolution is, potentially, the next step. All behaviour is to some degree context dependent. All teachings are informed by the time and place within which they are delivered. There are clear cultural contexts that inform methods of practice. Methods of practice are simply means to experientially realise the nature of reality as totality.

So what are these thirteen key-points, the 13 C's that are worthy of attention?

- Consciousness
- Complexity
- Core
- Communication
- Conscious community
- Creativity
- Childcare and Education
- Compassion
- Cultivating pleasure
- Currency
- Carbon-silicon interface
- Comedy
- Conflict resolution

The 13 C's:

- Consciousness - self reflection and knowing one's deepest identity as pure awareness.

- Complexity - of organisation and systemic relationships.

- Core - our vertical bipedal relationship to gravity.

- Communication - an evolutionary art.

- Conscious community - the only way we can survive as a species.

- Creativity - the capacity to make tools, art, and new worlds.

- Childcare - how we facilitate the development of future generations.

- Compassion - the ability to deeply feel, to be touched and moved by another's existence and condition.

• Cultivating pleasure - the desire to give and receive pleasure.

• Currency - the methods and means of resource access and movement.

• Carbon-silicon interface - the evolution of artificial intelligence and how we interface this with our own carbon based, DNA rich, neurologically complex bio-computer.

• Comedy - the aptitude to self reflect and generate humour out of the context in which we find our self.

• Conflict resolution - how we choose to utilise and transform the energies of conflict.

If this evaluation is sufficiently accurate then we could explore and follow the evolutionary way, or dharma, by paying conscious attention and intention in these key areas of evolutionary transition.

Let's continue this journey of 'yoga as conscious evolution' by asking,

"How and why are we human beings currently the dominant species on this planet?"

We clearly don't have big teeth, defensive armour, fur to keep us warm or vicious claws. How did we even survive as a spe-

cies?

If you believe we were directly 'created' by some divine power, or believe we are alien spirits inhabiting human form, or some other permutation of 'we are anything but descended from some prior mammals' then best not read on, it will be of no real interest to you. If, like us you can look at your own nipples, your own body in the mirror and recognise that we are a wonderful and interesting species of bipedal vertical mammal, then please read on. If you are interested by the factors that led to us being the dominant life-form, then read on. If you are interested in where we might be heading, then please read on.

As previously mentioned, evolution is influenced by the environmental demands on organisms; we influence and strikingly transform our environment. We are therefore unconsciously and unwittingly playing a hand in our own evolution. If we could look at what factors affect evolution, is there anything we could pay attention to that would facilitate our conscious evolution? It is this question that has led to these thirteen keypoints in an effort for us to understand conscious evolution. This book does not seek to offer the definitive view on this vital topic. We're very open to alternative views and better ways to understand the complexity of the situation we find ourselves living in.

Get in touch with us, share your views and explore the possibilities of our situation together.

Consciousness

The first key-point of conscious evolution is about increasing levels of self-reflective consciousness

Less complex creatures eat, respire, move, reproduce, expire, and that's about it. Such simple creatures have reflexive unconscious and innate instinctual responses to the world around them. Plants also have an array of such reflexive responses to the world around them, they too are sentient. Indeed, at a micro level it is impossible to make any clear distinction between plants and animals. As lifeforms become more complex they take longer to develop processing power that includes a locus of identity. Locus of identity is a functional development that allows for continuity of experience and ongoing relationships. It is the locus of identity, or 'sense-of-self', that has experiences.

Remembered events (or the past), apprehension about the future, narratives and meaning making all revolve around this sense-of-self, which is the 'one who acts'. The sense-of-self becomes more robust and more complex as animals move into greater levels of socialisation. Now we have the sense-of-self that is a part of a group, it has its place, its stream of relating and all the stories and feelings associated with that.

It is useful for such a social creature to remember each relationship and each dynamic as this allows effective engagement in any future intra-group dynamics. The important role of story or narrative in our experience as humans reflects this.

In many animal groups social interaction can be stressful and

complex and lead to minimal reproductive success since it is mostly the alpha males and females who reproduce. In such groups there is a constant struggle to be one of the alphas, yet being in a group offers safety and identity. Outside of the group only isolation, uncertainty and death exists.

As human life emerges the initial consciousness as sense-of-self is with the family, the hunter-gatherer group. There is always the 'in-group' (us), and the 'out-group' (them). Being in the in-group offers identity and safety. The out-group is alien, wrong, and not to be trusted.

All the reflexive patterns of being in the world including the sense-of-self and our cultural conditioning (being part of the in-group) are unconscious. Any part of the neurological information flow that bubbles up out of the unconscious into the global workspace[25]. This arena of individuated consciousness allows us to voluntarily act and therefore is the seat of choice and, arguably, free will. We get to choose what to attend to or not, to some degree.

As the social human evolved through agrarian and industrial societies into the contemporary technological world, the possibilities of emergent-consciousness changed. Gradually, we could separate our sense-of-self from total identification with the qualities of the group, qualities such as social organisation and orthodox religion. Once achieved, we now have the possibilities of identifying with a level of consciousness where we can recognise each of us as being mutual and equal residents of this planet.

The movement from close proximity to nature through industrialised culture has led to a dissociation from any deep ecological level of consciousness. We have lost our place as part of nature. This is in the process of being reclaimed and deeply understood by many, in conjunction with the new possibilities of global consciousness, which are available to us all. This is by no means an authoritative outline of emergent consciousness. Emergent consciousness arises through the evolution of life-form and is dependent on this evolution. Conscious evolution recognises this process and works with cultivating this systemic, deep-ecological awareness along with global consciousness.

The insight that arises from an authentic and deep yogic practice is that the whole universe is a play of sentience. Initially it feels like there is sentience (consciousness/awareness) and there is movement of impermanent flowing things. These two sides to reality are often mentioned in yogic philosophies as purusha and prakriti or kshetra-jna and kshetra, consciousness and matter, principle and process, or emptiness and form. This level of awareness of cosmic consciousness is a fundamental realisation that places the emergence of individuated consciousness, as the sense-of-self, within the matrix of the deep sentience that is the cosmos.

The next level of realisation that occurs is that this play of the two, sentience and impermanence, multiplicity and unicity, is an illusion. Really the two are one inseparable matrix. Sentience and space and all movements of things as space are one beautiful exquisite dance.

So we have the evolution of consciousness that allows systemic or deep ecological realisation, that allows global consciousness and that finally opens as cosmic consciousness.

Cosmic consciousness is also systemic and global, all movement blissfully and intimately embraces all that is deeply still. Sentience and space are metaphorically seen and consciously

25. The global workspace is the operational arena of what we call 'consciousness'. It is the part of us that allows the experience of conscious decision making as an individual.

felt as lovers, lovers who are perpetually in orgasmic blissful embrace. One can see this in Tantric iconography.

Conscious evolution is systemic, it places us as impermanent organisms in a healthy relationship with our eco-systems.

Conscious evolution is global, it places us in mutual and cooperative relationships with all members of humanity and co-creates the unfolding of real global civilisation.

Conscious evolution is cosmic and ultimately realises the nature of reality as sentient space and spacious sentience, the two as one, the one as two.

Conscious evolution requires self-reflective process and knowing ones deepest identity as this awareness, as the pristine awareness that pervades the cosmos and is the cosmos.

We might also propose that a 'civilisation' that encourages attention and action towards conscious evolution, a civilisation that encourages and promotes systemic, global and cosmic consciousness, would be an advanced and civilised civilisation.

Who will co-create such a civilisation?

Complexity

The second key to conscious evolution pays attention to social complexity with its inherent demands for cooperation and an understanding of our common ground.

When we look at the stream of evolution we see that there has been an increase in complexity from evolutionary biology through palaeo-history to the present day. From single celled organisms evolution has flowed through to the more complex mammals such as us. Our physiological complexity is such that we can no longer regenerate parts of our bodies very well, unlike our ancestral amphibians. Amphibians can re-grow limbs. Reptiles can re-grow tails, even though they are nowhere near as good as the originals, their new tails function. We can re-grow skin, muscle and bone if it is damaged. We also constantly grow new neural synapses related to our experiences in the world, this is the root of neuroscience. As cognitive creative beings we are also learning how to grow new synthetic body parts for ourselves.

Increasing social complexity is also a theme of human history. From hunter-gatherers through to agrarian villagers, from barbaric feudal autocrats through to our more tolerant democracies, there is a general trend towards increasing complexity of both biological and social organisation. Understanding this flow of emergent complexity we can choose to consciously work with both aspects of this, biological and social.

Evolutionary flow can now be seen as the transformation of decision making structures and encouragement of self managing communities that transcend the need for autocratic dominance.

Competition is the aspect of a dynamic where one party wins. This does not honour the emerging complexity we find ourselves in. Cooperation in balance with appropriate competition or 'coopetition' is a way this can effectively be worked with as a win-win scenario. Generating global understanding of the common ground between us, and more cooperation and coopetition, will enable all citizens of this planet to contribute to our collective wellbeing with their full potential.

Having members of our species unable to meet their potential and unable to share their gifts is a waste of human resource. This waste occurs because material resources are being concentrated in the hands of the 'few', resources are then unavailable to provide for the necessary support and education of the 'many'. Is greed and competition any longer a particularly sensible or sustainable way to govern a planet?

The thing about dis-eases whether they are individual, epidemic, medical or social is that they have to be diagnosed before the appropriate medicine can be administered, in just the right dose. In our view, humanity is suffering from a bad case of separate-materialism with its symptoms of fear, greed, envy, nihilism and hatred. When we, humans, fully realise we are not separate, that indivisibility is how things really are, then cooperation and friendly coopetition becomes the way we do things, rather than some wacky 'off the wall' behaviour.

When we, humans, realise we are not separate, that indivisibility is how things really are, then the governance of the planet would not be left to vested interest groups, party politics, or corporations with questionable understandings of how things really are (inseparable, indivisible, vast seamless unicity as diversity) would it?

When we, humans, realise we are not separate, that indivisibility is how things really are, then seeking common ground and cultivating real civilisation rooted in greater consensus, compassion and transparent clarity of decision-making will probably be the norm.

So, the second key to conscious evolution is paying attention to complexity and creating real civilisation rooted in conscious evolution. The inherent demands of this are for cooperation, coopetition and understanding the common ground. Each individual able to contribute and share their gifts effectively along with a culture of consensus and transparent clarity in decision-making. This could well be the way forward, what are your thoughts?

We say, let's bring it on, let's consciously evolve…

The Core

The third key is the vertical core line which is uniquely human. No other creature we know has been truly human.

With their flat feet, long iliac pelvic bones, and lumbar spine that cannot extend sufficiently to allow vertical bipedal movement even the apes cannot walk upright like we do.

Vertical bipedal movement means that when we walk we are imbalanced 80% of the time. Our body is loaded on just two points of contact and the vertical compression through our system presents different challenges to those experienced by quadrupeds.

One of these challenges in modern living is the collapse of the 'front line'. With no skeletal structure between the ribs and pelvis the front line collapses with gravity inhibiting the abdomen, breath efficiency and the pelvic floor. A chronic version of this might also include pronation of the feet, medially rotated hips, lordotic lumbar spine and anteriorly rotated shoulders, as well as a head pushed forward whilst suspended on the upper trapezius and spinal muscles that can no longer be used to move the head.

This sort of collapse is a recipe for physiological, skeletal, and muscular problems. The collapse into forward flexion in the body is also the physical response to fear and stress.

The solution?

The solution is to engage in practices that enable the familiarisation and balance of the forces of gravity in the body throughout its structure. Helpful practices that facilitate the flexible tissues of the myofascia to remain elastic and encourage optimal function.

Central nervous system management allied to fascial fitness and balanced with practices for the ancient enteric nervous system all lead to a quality of life that makes sense of our increased longevity. Various practices that complement this are meditation, mindfulness, yoga, pilates, fascial fitness, and tai chi. The increasing levels of empirical support for some of these practices points to their value.

Fascially oriented movement practices are being proven to support the human bipedal form into older age, leading to positive health and wellbeing. Meditation has been linked to positive epigenetic effects and increases in telomeres. This increase in the size of telomeres is related to increased longevity. With increased longevity we need increased quality of life. Quality of life grows through mindful living.

Mindful living is the requisite step before living as presence, as pure awareness.

So, when you walk be aware of the miraculous process of placing one foot in front of the other. When you talk be aware of the role of standing that led to the need for socialising that led to the need for advanced communication. As you use your hands be aware that vertical bipedal movement freed up our hands to allow for the use of tools, to touch, to eat, and to share as you do.

So much is taken for granted. Instead, let's step into the light of conscious evolution.

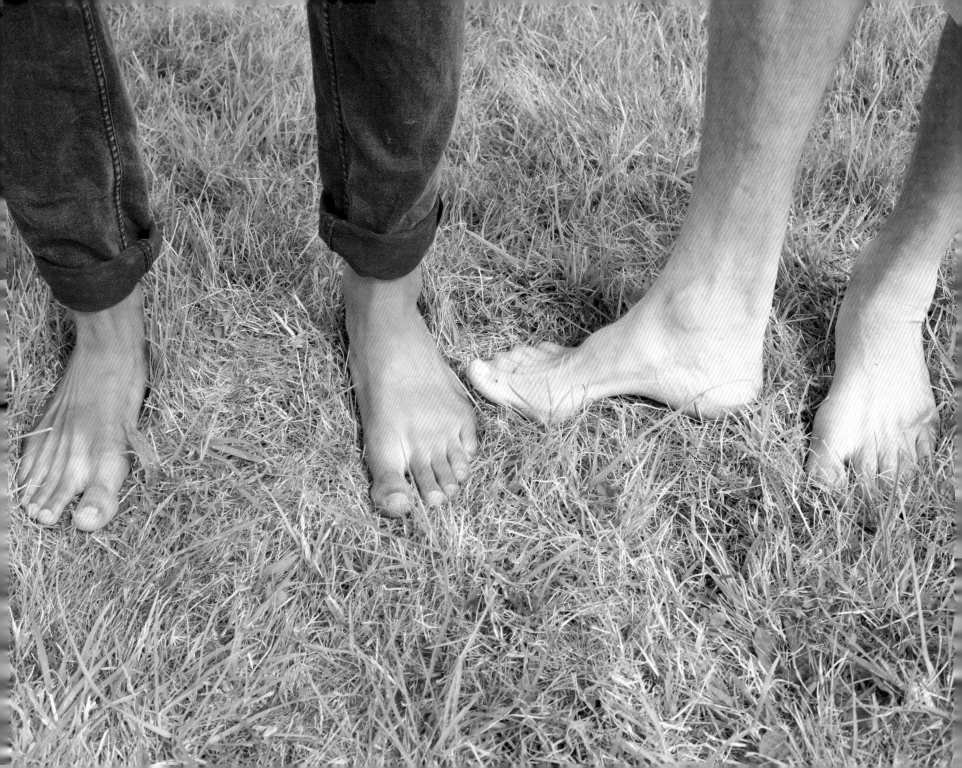

Communication

The fourth key-point of conscious evolution is the art of communication

The art of communication is an evolutionary art. The voice box and co-evolved cerebral cortex, which is capable of deciphering the complexity of sounds, the facial expressions and gestures we make, are all other reasons why we are currently the dominant species on this planet.

To flow consciously with evolution we would do well to enhance this and fully develop the art of communication. We are always in communication, even if we say nothing we are still communicating. The question is, what do we want to be communicating? Much human communication is still unconscious, reflexive and obsessively focused around obsessive, egocentric and ethnocentric viewpoints.

To cultivate the art of communication several elements appear useful. We have identified the following thirteen facets of this rich jewel, the art of communication.

1. Interoception – the capacity to sense deeply into our own biological system and listen to its needs and desires.

2. Emotional intelligence – the capacity to know our own feelings and be able to effectively and clearly communicate them.

3. Sit with feelings - To be able to sit with our feelings and not respond to them reflexively. You will then not be making

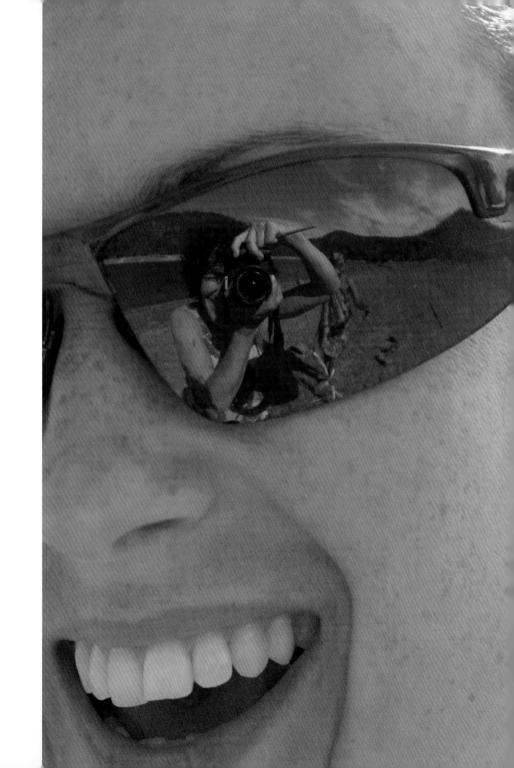

addictive demands on others based on your flow of feelings.

*4.   Heart based listening – the capacity to
deeply listen to all the parts of oneself and others
from a place of unconditional love.*

*5.   Empathy of understanding – understanding that we are all
learning to love, all learning to live in love. Understanding that
we all make mistakes and that this is a large part of learning.*

*6.   Desire to explore - consciously understanding and being
playful with our non-verbal communication, our body language
and pheromonal communication. We are then more willing to
play in the theatre of love and less likely to take it all personally.*

*7.   Knowing our deepest identity - when we know
who we are as 'Super-consciousness'[26] we wont be
grasping at anything to feel safe. In this way fear
and her many children[27] are slowly eliminated from
communication. What remains is love and awareness.*

*8.   Knowing we are all in this together - we
consistently seek the common ground.*

*9.   Give up the blame game – we understand the complexities
of flow so that we no longer seek to apportion responsibility
for arising problems in other people's 'back yards', nor in our
own. Our primary focus is now positive and solution focused.*

*10. Willingness to suspend our own 'viewpoints' for the greater
collective good - this capacity and willingness is balanced with*

*an understanding that our viewpoints, if clearly expressed,
may well serve the collective good. This is the art of consensus.*

*11. An abiding interest in conflict resolution - rather
than conflict creation, continuity of conflict, or conflict
management. Who does conflict serve? The art of
mediation is a facet of the art of communication.*

*12. Wise discrimination – the art and practise of
value, knowing what is truly important.*

*13. Sustain a good sense of humour – sense of humour deficit is
often a sign that we are starting to take it all a bit personally!*

What else might be useful to add?

The fourth key-point is the evolutionary art of communication.

26. Or Buddha Nature if you prefer that label, or any other label that helps us to understand we are the very nature of inseparability.

27. Greed, jealousy, anger, anxiety, envy, hatred, warfare, aggression, violence and withdrawal are all the children of fear.

Conscious Community

The fifth key-point of conscious evolution is the art of community

Authentic yoga is conscious evolution and conscious evolution is always workable. We can touch it, feel it and work with it. These key-points are simply intended as a method to begin to feel and see the issues we face and offer a first step. This work is not intended to be prescriptive, it is intended to encourage inquiry and promote insight that will allow us all to work in conscious flow with evolution. Flow with evolution allows us to thrive in the changing conditions we face. The alternative, given our capacity to dominate and destroy our environment is potentially partial or total extinction.

No matter what we do we are never not in community. Lets say that again as it is so important to understand, no matter what we do we are never not in community. Even those sitting in caves are in community, the breath they breathe is also our breath. Community is those we know and love, those we live amongst and those we share this planet with. Community in this sense is the concentric circles of the interdependent web of connection. Community is the place of communion, the spatial and temporal centre for shared existence. Without community there is no humanity. We are a relational species. We do not exist without community. The art of community is growing beyond unconscious and into conscious community.

To understand conscious community we need to know the deepest truth of existence. This 'truth' as vibrant livingness is simply that we are, in essence, pure awareness. Older traditions have variously called this Brahman, Buddha, Shiva, God, Goddess, Sat-chid-ananda, Original Nature and the Ubgrund.

This 'Truth'[28] is that each one of us is beginninglessly enlightened non-dual essence, continuously evolving as awakened process. Community (Sangha or Kula[29]) is also a method, a method through which each of us supports this arising of living as truth. Community becomes the vehicle and the expression of Conscious Evolution. We become a community of Buddhas and Buddhas to Be.

What does such a community offer?

Such a community offers sanctuary, support, challenge, communion and celebration.

Sanctuary is a place where we can rest in the experience of love, presence and awakened community.

Challenges, as necessary, from our loving celebrants of community, help us to remain in presence, awareness and responsibility.

Support helps us face our challenges and issues, whilst deepening in practices of yogic method, and in insight and realisation.

Communion is the sharing of love, realisation and deep joy.

Celebration is the coming together in joy, appreciation and gratitude of the members of the community and collectively sharing and expressing this.

How do we grow such community?

28. The word 'Truth' is a nominalisation, a way we turn vibrant process into something solid and defined, a noun. Truth, here, is a verb not a noun!

29. Sangha and Kula are Sanskrit terms for communities of realisers and realised beings.

Honesty, integrity, presence, awareness and willingness
to both communicate and take responsibility for
all of our thoughts, feelings and behaviours is what
allows the development of yogic community.
We each have to take individual responsibility for
all of 'our' thoughts, feelings and behaviours and the
consequence and impact of these in the world.
No one else is to blame, no one makes us think, or feel,
or do anything. As community members we assume total
responsibility for resolving 'our' conditioning and yet rest in
the openness and sustenance of the community of realisers.
To sustain such openness we cultivate integrity, profound
awareness and willingness to face the truth of what is,
with radikal inquiry and ruthless compassion.
Conscious community then becomes the community of the
realisers. We make manifest, we make real, conscious evolution.

Who is your conscious community?

When, how and with whom will you co-create, through your
commitment and involvement, conscious community in a sustain-
able and integral way?

Together, as conscious community, we recognise we are all
in this together, and we play, work and share together to help
each other discover our unique way of moving deeper into the
vision and realisation of 'Truth'.

Conscious community is realised inter-dependence in action.

Conscious community is a mirror reflecting back our
strengths, weaknesses and blind spots, if we are prepared to see
them. We see and know who we are, reflected in the hearts and
minds of every other member of the community.

Conscious community offers the possibility of a richer way
into our own hearts and minds.

Living more and more fully in the heart of our being, we find
mutual support in each other's struggles and successes, in each
other's development and simple pleasures.

Conscious community offers the possibility of consciously
co-creating culture and the future.

Members share commitment to each other's growth and
development in conjunction with a commitment to the wellbeing and mutual growth of the community.

Members support each other as they reveal and resolve shadow.

Members take responsibility for their psycho-emotional states
and for the wellbeing of the community.

Members seek common ground, resolution, responsibility,
greater love, deeper wisdom, more joy, more peace and com-
munal stewardship of this earth.

Members celebrate each other's joy and success.

Members share love and learn to live in love. Love is simply
the feelings of consciousness.

Are you ready for the journey and path of loving responsibility?

Do you want to practice the art of community?

What is stopping you?

The fifth key-point is the art of conscious community.

Creativity

We would like to pass on a habitable and beautiful planet to our children and our children's children. Why pass on a desecrated, polluted, war torn and embattled planet when we are capable of so much more?

The sixth key-point of conscious evolution is enhanced creativity

We are the first mammal with fully opposable fingers and thumbs. This allows us to manipulate objects and make tools. Of course this capacity is connected to a cerebrum that can take creative perspectives. These perspectives allow us to take a step back, up, or aside in our mind and view any object or process from a new, different or abstract angle. It is this new perspective connected to our desire and interest that allows us to fashion both tools and make art.

We are the art-making mammal. No other creature makes art in this way; all other creatures that appear to be creative, such as bower-birds are merely driven by innate drives.

It is this creative capacity to abstract our viewpoint and temporarily dissociate (from an object or process) that can also be subverted by egoic drives into destructiveness. The shadow side of our artistic capacities is our ability (and tendency?) to take things personally and create new means of destruction, torture and degradation for those who are 'different' - different tribe, different nation, different religion, different family or different whatever. We also make egoic positions and 'others' out of any perceived difference. We can also make art out of any perceived difference. The choice is ours!

So, what is creativity?

Creativity is, perhaps, an inspired response to phenomena from the experience of being human, as our friend Loren puts it. It is certainly arising out of a basic interest in phenomena. We have to be interested in something and cultivate an affinity with it to begin to manipulate and see its potential. We also have to assume two positions:

• The first is the place of abstraction so we can move the object around in our mind-scape.

• The second is the combined willingness, desire and ability to thoroughly engage with the material we are investigating. We have to be willing to explore and play. This is as true of sculpture, music and painting as it is of creative technology and creative environmental and social systems.

Art is a flow of interest and engagement. Your life is your art in this sense, and the 'canvas' is your mind-scape, your feeling-scape, your body, your relationships and your environment.

How will you craft your art of love and sparkling wisdom out of life?

Maybe life is art, period. Sadly, many of us don't get it and keep painting everything in their world grey or magnolia! 'Life sculpting' [30] *is what we can choose to do when we begin to recognise the spacious freedom between stimulus and response. It is this space whether we feel it in the mind, heart or both that we can then drop into, move from, dance with and sculpt our lives and our world, let's do this.*

The sixth key-point is enhanced creativity. Let's explode our creativity…

30. Yinke Tuakli calls the offering of his work Life Sculpting, as different from coaching and such.

Childcare and Education

The seventh key-point of conscious evolution is childcare and education

The most important task for our species and culture is raising the next generation. All other activity and business supports this aim. One might think this wasn't the case given the low levels of funding and resource allocated, and the minimal priorities given to this crucial evolutionary role. Are we more interested in filling our children with our views on religion, work, money, life and love than truly facilitating their learning. Real learning allows them to respond freely and creatively to the future conditions they will face, future conditions we cannot even begin to apprehend. We don't know what the future holds, so imposing what we feel children need is potentially wasting and disregarding their creative and responsive skills.

We've looked at the hypothalamic pituitary axis (HPA), the line of mid-brain and glands through the core of the body.

We've looked at how the response thresholds of the HPA are set up in the first six-months of life.

We've looked at how this setting up of the HPA informs future perspectives and responsive patterns.

We've looked at how the physical and emotional holding of the baby, how it is communicated with, how it is held, and the level of loving physical contact it receives, all affect how this HPA is set up.

We've looked at how the lower thresholds of stress response set as a default in infancy prepare for the probability of a life lived in a stressed state. All the complex relationship issues and disease possibilities that arise with a low threshold of stress response then sadly follow.

We've looked at how to build a cortisol rich brain with a low threshold HPA through ignorance, un-love, neglect and abuse.

We've looked at how cortisol toxified brains cannot maximise the synaptic connections and communicative capacities between brain regions. It is this possibility of clearer communication between brain regions that is the key difference between a stressed baby and a more relaxed, relatively cortisol free, baby.

We've looked at how cortisol rich brains also have less pleasure receptors, and so experience less pleasure as well as being less cognitively adept, less emotionally intelligent and less intellectually responsive.

We've also looked at how to facilitate a relaxed HPA in an infant with a brain that maximises its potential neuronal connections.

We've also looked at how an authentic and intelligently applied yogic practice can eventually reset the HPA, build new pleasure receptors, and craft new neurological connections that may have been absent previously. This is the nature of self-applied neuroplasticity, which is what yoga and meditation offer.

However, why do the rehabilitation when prevention is possible?

What would you rather have for your child? A happy life or a decade or more of therapeutic engagement so one can manage a relationship?

The level of therapeutic practice required to rebuild the HPA is not small. If one is devoted to somatic, emotional, cognitive and vibrational awareness practices, as well as a therapeutic relationship, it can be possible to achieve such reconditioning of the nervous system (over many years). A person also has to be fortunate enough to come across teachings and practices that facilitate such change, and sadly this is not common.

Watching children grow, we are fascinated by their sparkling intelligence at very early ages. Our culture tells us that children are empty brains ready for conditioning, ready to be filled with information. Parenting tells us that children are wonderfully responsive and creative beings whose bright intelligence informs every single interaction they have. They are so communicative that they create body and sound languages from a really early age, languages that their really close family will understand.

If these communications are missed the child will, with the inattention it receives, shut down its sparkling genius when met with blank responses. If a child's endeavours to communicate are consistently missed or ignored it will not make the synaptic connections that grow its brain. These connections reflect the relational and communicative genius it is, and we all are, and it is these key love relationships that teach the child who it is.

Parents who are too busy chasing profit and unable to see their child's communicative attempts due, perhaps, to their own insensitivity or too stressed to pay attention effectively, miss these vital developmental opportunities for their children. Parents who hand over their children to carers, even to the most highly trained of nursery staff, miss this vital opportunity for their children.

Nursery staff cannot pay the same loving attention in the way that a parent, saturated with dopamine and other neurotransmitters of love, can. Nursery staff cannot be expected to tune into each individual child's micro-developmental language, this is unreasonable, especially if they are looking after many children. In such environments, even with the best will in the world, the children slowly shut their synaptic possibilities down from the absence of the appreciative, responsive gaze of the significant adults in their life. It is of course usually mother or father who are the significant adults, and who most deeply understand their child.

Why would any parent miss this special time for themselves and their children simply to maximise their profit? What a crying shame for both parents, children and culture.

When a culture understands that all its children are its children and that all its children are its future, then maybe this will change?

We understand the stages of child development very well. We have models of education from many sources, each of which has strengths and weaknesses. Some specialise in creativity and being comfortable in nature, others teach effectively about mathematics but lack exposure to myth and creativity. Some focus on project learning or pattern recognition. Some styles of education focus on agendas that are to be measured by various mechanisms that appear to be more about measurement systems, rather than about the child's actual development. We also know that a dollar spent in childhood on effective and affective education is worth thousands of dollars spent later on social services, criminal justice and rehabilitation programmes.

So, if we are to co-create an enlightened world and an enlightened education then prioritising resources towards childcare and education is crucial. Finding the strengths in each educational approach and each individual child, with less focus on the weaknesses, will offer us a comprehensive and broad approach to the education we can offer our future generations.

Education that offers creativity, comfort and presence in nature, effective development in mathematics, science and literacy, pattern recognition, cognitive skills, emotional literacy, somatic intelligence and spatial skills can all be brought into an enlightened education.

Understanding neurological development and neuroplasticity, we would prioritise all the skills that lead to a balanced brain development. Balanced brain development would most probably include the following for all children to realise their potential:

- *Child centred, project based explorations*

- *Appropriate touch*

- *Subject/object relations and core identity*

- *Communication skills*

- *Self-esteem*

- *Intra-personal skills*

- *Interpersonal skills*

- *Appreciation*

- *Creativity*

- *Critical thinking*

- *Basic life skills, including creating beautiful food and caring for oneself*

- *Numeracy and mathematics*

- *Literacy*

- *Other languages*

- *Somatic intelligence and body skills*

- *Spatial intelligence*

- *Musical intelligence*

- *Understanding and working with their own mind and meditative mind training*

- *Emotional intelligence*

- *Self-directed learning skills*

- *Ecological intelligence*

- *Explorations in human belief*

- *Global citizenship, rights and responsibilities*

- Understanding science

- *Exploring global history*

- *Information technology*

- *Central nervous system management skills*

- *Positive psychology*

Some educational analysts would add financial intelligence. However in our enlightened economy, maximising profit and accumulating personal wealth will be of minimal consequence. Cultivating, developing and giving one's greatest gifts and facilitating the full potential of all will be what life is all about.

Flowing into conscious evolution, aware of this key-point, we will be looking at clear ways to help the next generation be prepared to meet the changing conditions they will most certainly face. The world will be as it is, we have no real way of knowing what that might be, beyond guesswork, intuition and belief, and this is not enough. By preparing our children with creativity, critical thinking and other skills they will know what to do and how to deal with the changes they face.

What else do you feel would facilitate healthy, holistic child-centred learning that will prepare our future generations in the best possible way?

Compassion

The eighth key-point of conscious evolution is compassion

Invertebrates, fish, amphibians and reptiles do not emote. They have nervous systems that feel gratification or satisfaction and of course they experience pain. These two basic drives of the separate feeling nervous system are common to all of life. Plants sense and move with light, they are phototropic. Plants also sense and respond to gravity, they are geotropic. Plants sense vibration, emit vibration and have tactile senses. Plants also communicate through complex underground root, mycorhizzal, and bio-chemical communicative systems.

All of life has the basic drives that yogic psychology speaks of as raga and dvesha. These two drives, in English, are craving and aversion. These two primary drives are the foundation of the self-sense. In humans we have a third drive, a third way our self-sense makes sense of the world and this 'ego' drive is moha or ignorant indifference. Living beings seek to draw some things into themselves and push others away.

Humans, failing to pay attention to the reality of inseparability, behave as if they are disconnected from everything else and treat events, experiences and apparent others as if they are irrelevant, this is moha.

More primitive life-forms simply do not have the brain structure to feel and experience emotions. We humans love to anthropomorphise all creatures, especially the furry ones. We make other beings behave as if they were humans in our mind.

This is the world according to Pixar and Disney. Many birds such as crows and all mammals exhibit the brain structures for emotional bonding and the navigation of the world of intra-specific relationship through emotion. Fishes and reptiles often eat their own children, mammals and more advanced birds rarely do so. They will, however, eat each other's children. For example, male tigers will kill the children of another male when they take over a new female. Cetaceans, whales and dolphins have been around for 28 million years and have brains with much greater coalescence between the emotional and cognitive aspects. They probably do not separate emotion and cognition in the way we do. As reasonably advanced primates we have been around for 2 million years. Our brains, which are also still in the process of evolution, have emotional capacities to feel connected, to empathise and feel compassion and love.

Long-term meditators, who have been tested with brain scanning devices, evidence brains that can work differently to folk who have never meditated or developed awareness and compassion practices. The left pre-frontal cortex and emotional centres, along with higher levels of gamma-synergy, appear to be more active in regular meditators who also evidenced greater levels of compassion.

So what is compassion?

• Sympathy is generally thought of as a feeling of pity or sorrow for someone else's misfortune.

• Empathy is the ability and behaviour of understanding and sharing the feelings of another.

• Compassion is the ability of understanding another's situation coupled with appropriate action and behaviour to facilitate as much change in that situation as is possible for that other person.

There is a possible development, a progression of understanding and action in the realisation of inseparability through the process of these three feeling states. We view compassion as more advanced than empathy, which is more developed than sympathy. Compassion is a skill-set. There have been many different measures and scales of moral behaviour and development proposed by psychologists. They all consider moral development to be founded in treating and behaving towards other beings with mutual regard. A morally developed brain behaves differently to a more selfishly functioning brain.

There is a common mistake over what compassion really means in terms of one's daily practice and life in the world. Compassion is not about seeking Disney style happy endings for everybody, not about everybody getting their fair slice of cream cake. This style of compassion doesn't recognise that everything is impermanent flow and that everything is empty of inherent separate existence, and wants to cuddle everything and turn the whole world into fluffy teddy bears, care bears and unicorns. This, though quite sweet at its best, can be nauseating at its neoliberal worst, and can be helpfully understood as 'idiot compassion'.

Real compassion recognises that all things change, that all apparently separate beings die and that there is no separate intrinsic existence to any apparently separate being. It is from this basis in 'reality' that real compassion begins.

So, yes, real compassion seeks to actively reduce unnecessary pain whilst recognising that pain is an inevitable consequence of residence as a nervous system. Real compassion also seeks to help all beings understand that suffering is entirely optional. This is where the real compassion becomes so powerful because it means we can choose to do something about suffering, we can eliminate it from our own experience and we can help and encourage others to do the same.

How do we eliminate suffering?

Simple! We stop inhabiting the separate self-story as if it were the deepest truth of our existence. The self-story is a neurological contraction of our possibilities that positively serves as a vehicle to navigate the experience of form and the appearance of separation. At its worst, the self-story becomes our most cherished identity, one that requires defence, defiance, justification, and an aggressive modus operandi in the world to get what 'I' need and never mind anyone else, unless they are also 'mine', my friends, my family, my country, my religion, my, my, mine.

Living as a self-story in the world of impermanent flow is eminently unsatisfactory. We can never truly win, never finally possess, and never really be safe unless we eventually get that we are nobody, we are not that self-story.

When we know that we are not this neurological fantasy, this contraction, then we don't need to defend or attack or justify in that same old way. When we embrace that each of us is deliciously riddled with feelings, that we are all rather tentative about dying, we can begin to be compassionate, can we not?

Real happiness and joy can only begin when the relentless dissatisfaction of the grasping, shoving, withdrawing, fearful and indifferent ignorance of the self-contraction is seen for what it always was - an evolutionary phase and neurological fantasy, one that facilitated a particular period of human development that we're now evolving beyond, aren't we?

Since we mention development, idiot compassion would have every being seen as developmentally equal. We are not. Real compassion sees the developmental level of any individual as appropriate, at the right time, in the right way, and lovingly offers the developmental medicine for that individual to facilitate their own development. Real compassion helps beings grow beyond all versions of holding a position in space-time and become nobody. We recommend becoming nobody and nothing, become inconsequential. Only now can we see and know that all beings are potentially equal. All beings can develop and move from 'Buddhas to Be' out of their contraction, pain and suffering, leave behind the distorted influences around which they built their self-story and finally be Buddhas, awakened ones. Real compassion leads this journey into inevitable inconsequence and is the force of consciousness moving through the affective aspect of inseparability.

So, what has love got to do with it?

Love is such a loaded word, partly because it means so many things to so many people. Love has correlations from loving ice-cream through to unbearable passion for a lover, and to the feeling of a vast benevolent universe as a function of some creative principle. Both compassion and love in all its forms require presence, they are both facets of being fully here, now, present and spacious, aware of all the ramifications through space-time of each and every thought, feeling and action. This is what presence implies.

Love then is the feeling of presence, it is the feeling aspect of consciousness. Authentic compassion is the direct experience of developmental understanding and appropriate action to relieve unnecessary pain. Authentic compassion seeks to resolve suffering and facilitate the movement of all beings into the intelligent dissolution and transcending of the self-contraction so that each being discovers their natural state as awakened presence, moving in the world as love and compassion.

Love is the deepest feeling-wisdom of inseparability. Compassion is a key aspect of conscious evolution. Compassion is the active recognition of indivisibility, and it is the eighth key-point in conscious evolution.

Love is…

Cultivating Pleasure

The ninth key-point of conscious evolution is cultivating pleasure

The clitoris is the only organ in the whole of evolution solely devoted to pleasure. The clitoris is not just the nerve rich button sitting above a woman's Yoni[31]. It is also the deep structure rooted through into the G-spot and the vaginal walls as a web of nerves and erectile tissue, a multi-limbed structure all evolved to facilitate pleasure and ecstatic bliss (potentially).

The nerves in the glans penis of the male are much less in number and much more localised to the tip of the penis, although the analogous erectile tissue is obviously present.

Through physical yoga practise, breath work, meditation, sexual yogas and loving relationship (with self and/or other/s) one understands sexuality to be a loving sharing of love. We know that the feelings of pleasure and bliss arising through the genitals can be extended into the totality of the physical and energetic bodies and beyond.

What has this got to do with evolution?
What has this go to do with yoga even?

In most animals the procreative act is a time of great danger, both male and female are vulnerable and potential lunch. In gorillas, for example, the penis contains a bone to facilitate rapid ejaculation from the relatively tiny penis. Biological sexual drives are innate and serve to combine gametes as quickly as possible, and get back to the business of eating. As the joke about some men's sexuality goes, it's like the panda - eats, shoots and leaves.

The development of the clitoris in human females along with face-to-face mating and the development of language allow a whole new realm of pleasurable possibility. For sure the essential genetic drives are similar, to deliver seeds from the male, receive seeds into the female and incubate the next generation. However, with the ascendancy of the human species we now also have the opportunity to celebrate the sexual act as a means of cultivating and sharing ecstatic pleasure, bliss, connection and inseparability.

The sexual act, devoid of emotional integrity, has been used as a political tool of domination and of control. Various abuses such as shame, guilt, propaganda, media portrayals, and genital mutilation have been the means exercised by politicised religions to destroy the beauty, power and validity of loving sexuality as a form of worship.

So we are talking about polar opposite experiences using the same process - sexuality. One is loving and evolutionary, the other abusive, oppressive and controlling.

All patriarchal religions have sought to control women, their sexuality and reproduction, and prioritise the descent of property through the male line. Many men are unnerved by women's sexual drives and women's capacity for orgasm. Men have historically evidenced fear of the mighty yoni and/or a desire to control and destroy its power. This has been done through endless permutations of misogyny from political domination, patriarchal religions and their narratives, all the way to witch burnings, stoning and female genital mutilation.

---

31. Yoni is a Sanskrit term that refers to the vagina, womb and the creative space of the universe.

And it's still happening today.

It's happening through grotesque objectification in the contemporary western world, where what matters most about a woman is clearly not her art, her mind or her life but the shape of her body. If you don't believe this please read any tabloid newspaper.

Bearing all of this in mind, if a child grows up in stressful situations then one of the brain's responses to these conditions is to reduce the number of pleasure receptors. Pleasure receptors occur more in brains that have developed in environments of ease, acceptance, love, tactile holding, emotional contact and celebration - of pleasure and the individual. What else could we expect?

The capacity to feel and enjoy pleasure deeply is the result of a well developed brain. For those who have brains that are deficient in pleasure receptors certain gentle pleasure practices, sadhanas[32], such as massage and erotic exploration can be highly beneficial to re-establish the brain's riches of natural pleasure receptors.

How can a brain closed to ordinary levels of endorphins be expected to open in ecstatic bliss?

Pleasure can be skilfully, tenderly and lovingly used as a therapeutic tool to facilitate a more pleasure receptive brain and a higher quality of life, can't it?

There is also a big difference between pleasure in service of the ego as basic hedonism and self-gratification versus pleasure as a tool of service to allow an individual's neurology to open

32. Individualised transpersonal developmental practices. The Sanskrit root 'sadh' ot the word 'sadhana' means effort. Sadhana therefore requires effort and application, it is method.

to love and bliss as a means of transcending the self-structure. Literally it can be a yogic path to blow one open to bliss-emptiness to divine realisation, we know this is true, and we trust you will/do too.

There is a big difference between lust divorced from love, and love spiced by the raw juiciness of lust. Lust for awakening is why we are all on the path of yoga.

Flowers hanging off the trees in springtime are the genitals of plants, we give them, unconsciously perhaps, as symbols of love and beauty. How have we got into such a cultural pickle where mostly people see their own and others genitalia with shame, guilt and as symbols of disgust with basic bodily function?

This is slowly changing, even though the old paradigm of body-negative feeling and thinking still dominates much of the global world-view.

Yoga has three strands. One being Sutra, and another Tantra.

These are our definitions, which are also supported by 'tradition' should you need that.

Sutra Is…
Sutra is the practice of cultivating realisations of impermanence, inter-dependence and emptiness. This requires psycho-emotional clarity be maximised, and engagements and distractions minimised, so that one can deeply compute these three realisations.

The Three Realisations…

Firstly, impermanence means that physical existence is limited, death can occur at any time, termination will happen. The first stage of realisation is to really 'get' this truth and live with this recognition embedded in our neurology.

We have to stop pretending we are physically immortal and engage with life from a place of honest fragility and vulnerability. If we wait to die before we recognise the blindingly obvious its a bit late!

The compassion in our heart that arises and radiates from the recognition of this unguarded truth allows deeper human intimacy and less pretence. There are no winners in impermanence.

Secondly, inter-dependence is the living gnosis that nothing in this flow is separate from any other thing. Every-thing is visibly intertwined if we look closely enough. All 'things' are really only appearances. What this means is that nothing in itself has any solid, permanent, defined or separate existence. What we view as solid 'reality' is scintillating shades of the continuum of matter (as vortices of energy) and flowing energy such as we find in the electro-magnetic spectrum.

This living systemic quantum-ecology requires that we share our contributions with the world in a more cohesive and less brutal way. We are no longer the dominators or owners of the planet, we are part of the flow of life and independence becomes known to be illusory.

This brings the third realisation into place - emptiness.
We know there is no inherent, separate, continuous, defined or permanent existence to any-thing, including our bodies, feelings, thoughts, self-sense, pleasure, pain and so on. If we look deeply into any-thing, we find no-thing solid. Nothing exists in itself, of it-self, all we find is no-thing. This is what 'emptiness' means. Every-thing is empty. Emptiness is every-thing and yet it cannot be found.

It is from the base of these realisations that Tantra in any authentic way can really begin, Tantra grows out of Sutra.

Tantra Is…

Traditional Tantra recognises the path to awakening as through the earthy and raw vitality of the feminine principle, the body and the flows of energy that constitute our world of appearance. This is simply because we begin where we are, to find the balance to the feminine principle we go through her. To reach sentience we explore energy, movement and space-time.

Mistakenly, many people want to define Tantra as this and that sort of sexuality. Really Tantra can only be initially defined in reference to the base of Sutra[33], so some understanding of Sutra (as above) is necessary. Arguably you cannot have Tantra without Sutra. Otherwise it's like trying to read a book without learning one's ABC. This of course will irritate all those who want Tantra defined simply in terms of sexuality.

Tantra is much, much more than just sexuality and way bigger than just being defined by the feminine principle. The feminine principle is usually translated in people's minds as the feminine gender and it's not the same thing either. Again you can't have Yin without Yang or vice versa.

So yes, the feminine principle is really important in Tantra

---

33. Sutra means Thread. Sutric practice is the cultivation of the basic skills of philosophical view, devotion and mind training.

as it is considered as the path, and this is the crux, the path to know the divine, the only authentic route of access to divinity. Divinity itself is the ecstatic balance of masculine and feminine principles. But She is the only way home!

Interestingly, Indian Tantra and Tibetan Tantra have the masculine and feminine principles in apparent opposition and contradiction.

Indian Tantra has consciousness as the male principle and energy and form as the female principle of space and movement.

Tibetan Tantra has the feminine principle as wisdom, as the pregnant emptiness that is the source of everything. The masculine principle in Tibetan Tantra is method. Method arises out of form, it is a function of space, time and movement and involves effort. Method is sadhana and is male. So we see that masculine and feminine in this sense are not fixed 'truths' but perspectives, teaching metaphors and methods of approach to and direct experience of the totality from the illusion of separation.

Tantra and Sex…

So we understand that Western Neo-tantra has extracted sexuality and posited it as the key practice of Tantra. We can also see that is a very limited perspective. Tantra is a lot bigger than sex and great orgasms!

Osho in his time wrote a book titled "From Sex to Superconsciousness" but as we so rightly know and as we teach, sex is Superconsciousness.

Everything is Superconsciousness, you cant go from sex to Superconsciousness. You can however get from sex as a dance of apparent opposites, as a play of polarities in various states of realisation to realisation of always and already Superconsciousness.

Yes most sex is unrealised, it is not realised as a divine play of Superconsciousness. This is what we're looking at growing as a global movement, that sexuality when 'realised', is prayer. Realised sexuality is 'worship'. Sex as love as bliss-emptiness is and always has been sacred.

Diamonds thrown to swine get trampled in the mud. Sex in the minds of those living in duality, as samsara, is largely a self-oriented activity of lust, hedonism and personal gratification. It has little to do with approaching reality as Superconsciousness.

Sutra defines and crafts the threads of realisation, whilst Tantra weaves those exquisite threads of realisation into the expansive non-dual tapestry of the always-already reality, as it is, Superconsciousness.

Pleasure and sexuality are plays of energy that the Tantrika[34] freely engages with. This practice deepens one's loving resonance and that communicates to all around us, literally we make love. We make the vibrations of love and communicate those through our world.

Tantric Yoga practice, as the technology of ecstasy, channels sexual energy. This channelling expands sexual energy beyond the limitations of the nervous system into the web of bio-electromagnetic flow that is also who we are.

This happens when we activate, energise, strengthen and clarify the flow through all the energy-lines of the body so that these primal energies of nature can roll through this system, expanding the neurological possibilities of bliss to proportions whereby the boundaries between the separate sense-of-self and the flow of energy that is also the cosmos become totally dis-

34. Tantrikas are practitioners of Tantra.

solved into ecstatic surrender as the One that is the many, the many as the One.

"Two become One and the whole is then (known as) holy" as Jivana Kennedy says.

Practices that facilitate this include somatic movement practices, breath practices, awareness practices, visualisation practices, sonic practices, vibrational practices and relational practices. The realisation arising as a result of such practices is the non-dual realisation of the radiant formlessness of the divine dancing as form.

These practices of pragmatic engaged sexuality have been called Red Tantra or the left hand path. This left hand path in all its various forms, has been consistently derided by institutionalised, dogmatically religious, celibate, and misogynistic men as low and unhelpful.

Certainly the White Tantra path of working with gaze and energy play is profound.

Certainly the Esoteric Tantra approach of working with visualisations of masculine and feminine energies as solar and lunar currents within one's own body are profound.

Yet as we see it and know it, it is largely anti-sexual prejudice and fear that decries the Red Tantra approach of working directly with a consort.

Weaving the energies of blissful ecstatic embrace through each other's hearts, opening each other's minds to the vast boundless reality and knowing each other as masculine and feminine essence in embrace as the whole cosmos is utterly profound too.

This route for the non-celibate Yogin is also a superior path and is a way for us to weave the neurologies of pleasure into bliss and bliss as emptiness to be known as the foundational nature of the cosmos. Red Tantra simply includes the practices of esoteric and White Tantra and brings them into full embodiment. One of the key tools of conscious evolution we have to really celebrate and explore reality is pleasure. Pleasure used in this way is a trans-egoic route to realisation.

Women as possessors of the finest organ ever evolved for pure pleasure lead the way here as priestess's of bliss. Women have always played this role, which is why patriarchal religions often despised them. Religions of masculist austerity cannot tolerate pleasure as a path or even as an aspect of life, hence fundamentalism in its many masculine flavours is usually brutally ascetic.

As inheritors of a masculist, protestant, pleasure hating culture we may do well to eliminate such stories from our cultural biology, our individual and collective psychology and fully celebrate the union of sexuality, pleasure, bliss and love with emptiness.

However the Sutric threads of realisation arise, and this is not necessarily through some institutionalised tradition, these threads remain the pre-requisites for the powerful and juicy dance of Tantra.

These prerequisites do have to be authentic realisation though not just imagination. Without these prerequisites in place Tantra (or Neo-tantra) results in a relentless chase for more endorphins and serotonin, we become nothing more than a junkie to our own neuro-chemicals and we become reliant on the appearance of 'others' on the 'outside' to gener-

ate them with us. Neo-tantra due to the lack of discipline and authentic realisation has a tendency to head into greater and greater sensation and less sensitivity.

Authentic Tantra will have us utterly responsible for our own neuro-chemistry and we rest in non-contextual bliss and deeper and deeper sensitivity and appreciation. Contemporary Tantra that includes all aspects of our existence in a rich exploration of the wonderful natural perfection of life is conscious evolution in practice.

Please do enjoy your Self and everyone else (as Self)... as long as it's mutual and consensual. This is the essence of the ninth key-point in conscious evolution.

Currency

Currency is the tenth key-point in conscious evolution

We humans have created systems of trade built out of basic barter since time immemorial. Instead of simply trading one resource for another such as furs for pig iron, or pottery for salt, we created a means of exchange we call money. To make money work an agreed value had to be placed on it so a fair exchange of so many deer hides for so many barrels of pig-iron could reasonably occur. After all the iron miner needed to know how much bread he could buy and the hide trader wanted to know how many deer he had to hunt before he could rest for the winter and make arrows. Collectively agreed value on certain phenomenon, such as gold, has been the means we have used to craft the basis of a system of trade. Gold has always been of special value, because it doesn't rust or tarnish and because it's reasonably rare that particular element has been treasured. Yet gold itself has no intrinsic value any more than copper, rust or dust.

The whole Semitic, Arabic and Christian world have at various points described usury as a crime against God. Usury is where you lend someone ten pounds and demand eleven back, you take a percentage of profit on what you lent. But, we hear you ask, isn't that the foundation of capitalism? Yes it is, capitalism is built on what was originally understood to be a crime against God and man. The criminal status of usury was lost under Protestantism. The Protestant church was originally

poor and to generate wealth it was consensually agreed that making money for God was a good thing. A mere couple of hundred years later the God bit was largely forgotten and just making money off money was a good thing! Capitalism was away, out of the starting blocks.

Money was later also de-linked from the gold standard and we are left with currency. Currency is worthless of itself, worth only what people believe it is worth, because currency has no real existence. Currency is in fact a virtual commodity that is manufactured out of thin air by organisations such as The World Bank, The Federal Reserve, The International Monetary Fund and other such private corporations. They simply decide how much currency a country is allowed and hey presto it exists. When a government has a new flood of currency, they then they lend it to the banks. The banks as private corporations can then can lend out twenty times that amount, so that virtual commodity created out of thin air is now twenty times as valuable, magnified by the banks to create even more of this virtual commodity. So magic tricks aside, why does this matter and what has it to do with yoga.

Yoga is conscious evolution. The social evolution of our species has focused very much on how to exchange and distribute resources and commodities. The system we have come up with so far was first barter, then money and now currency, and currency is simply what we trade our precious life-energy for. Given one is relatively restricted on this planet without currency and given that people will often do anything for more currency, how do we co-create a world where the positive effects of resource distribution outweigh the negative effects on human psychology that the desire for more and more currency clearly can have.

   Given we have a hugely inequitable planet and disparity in wealth contributes to massive suffering on the planet then four questions anyone looking at social engineering and human potential might ask are:

How will we design a fairer, more equitable system of resource allocation and distribution?

How are we are going to do build an enlightened economy?

How will we ensure that each individual has the best prospects for sharing their creative human potential?

What will our enlightened economy look and feel like?

   This remains to be seen. But Engaged Yoga practitioners are part of the process of crafting such a world with such an economy. It is a key-point in conscious evolution.

What part will you play?

Carbon-Silicon Interface

The eleventh key-point of conscious evolution is the carbon-silicon interface

The carbon-silicon interface is already happening. It might be wise for us to pay attention and work as creatively, effectively and honestly as we can with this reality. We as carbon based life-forms have created silicon based artificial intelligence, how we develop this interface is important. Of course a lot of this carbon-silicon interface is being used for 'defence' purposes.

The 'void junkies', those who misunderstand Jnana Yoga will say that it's all Maya, all illusion and none of this realm of changing flow matters. But then when we look into our own hearts, our own wisdom as well as the myriad of non-dual teachings from the Ishavasya Upanishad through Kasmiri Shaivism, Wei Wu Wei, Buddhist Tantra and quantum physics to dispel that foolish notion, we know that it's all real, it all matters.

We understand from our yoga practice nothing has inherence and that the perceptual stories we create from the limitations of the senses fabricate a world of substantiality, permanence and definition. When we understand the fractal interdependent matrix as the reality, then yes, all the separatist, materialist perceptual tales and views we tell ourselves about reality are blown away as the illusions they are, but it's still all real! So, we cultivate the tools to face and appreciate the pain, the bliss and the flow of impermanence.

The current carbon-silicon interface we are familiar with is the keyboard and the screen. The interface we are familiar with from science fiction is a much deeper neurological interface where the artificial intelligence of silicon and the organic intelligence of carbon based life-form (as homo-sapiens) merges in a range of cybernetic, cyborg and robotic possibilities that has always seemed far-fetched. It really is not that far fetched any more though. An old friend of Christopher's runs a business that has been working on voice recognition systems and these systems are getting much more effective. Credit card providers have a highly responsive system that seems to work very well. The vocal interface is a relatively new one that has been growing over the past ten years and has now landed as a part of our daily life. Researchers at Zhejiang University in Huangzhou, China have developed a small quadcopter that is flown fairly rudimentarily by thought alone. This system converts brainwaves via an EEG machine through to a laptop with software that then controls the copter. Interestingly rich in paradox, China with its environment being savaged by its ferocious industrial growth also leads the world in building eco-cities, a move that the west would do well to emulate.

The latest Paralympics in the UK was a most amazing event, a profoundly powerful and evolutionary event. Humans with a whole variety of differing abilities pushed the edges of possibility and proved their power, determination, athletic capacity and human value despite formidable obstacles and difficulties in achieving what they achieved. Can anyone who is not blind imagine participating in the blind long jump?

Artificial intelligence (AI) at the moment is only good at what it's good at, sounds silly but its true. AI focuses only on specific tasks, such as playing chess, finding web pages, flying drones and so on. AI currently lacks the capacity to act with generic intelligence. AI cannot yet complete the process of sensing its environment, gathering information, evaluating this information effectively, then modify it's knowledge base and it's perceptions and actions, whilst also act in a wide variety of modes based on this process. This process is what we do. This general intelligence appears far off in the world of AI, but is it? Ben Goertzel of OpenCog an open-source AI project suggests this level of AI is only ten to fifteen years away.

"Imagine an AI with sensors all over the planet, able to read thousands of web-pages and data sets at once and exchange data with other AI's via direct mind-to-mind file transfer" as Ben asks, because this is the way AI is heading.

A current theory of human individuated consciousness is called GWT. GWT stands for global workspace theory. Many autonomous brain regions harvest the sensory fields for information which only reaches what we call consciousness, or what this theory calls the GWT when it is deemed important enough. Software that mimics the human global workspace is currently working with up to twenty thousand neurons, which offer one and a half million connections. The human brain comprises around one hundred and twenty billion neurons offering trillions of synaptic connections. So AI has a long way to go.

But lets look at the primitive way humans behave on this planet, the primitive superstitious belief systems we give value to, the relentless tribal battles of country against country and the simple fact that most people are happy reading tabloid newspapers full of mammaries, bigoted opinion, hearsay and gossip. Not much productive use from that awesome bio-com-

puter then?

The principle of the neuro-bot that is being worked with is simply that getting one simple twenty thousand-neuron unit to work leads to a multiplicity of units where each unit is given responsibility for one simple function. Multiple units wired together gives a neuro-bot with several million neurons.

Following on from the Paralympics we already have the beginnings of nuero-linked prosthetics. We already wear computerised pacemakers and many other medical devices that support and measure life. Neuro-linked prosthetics connect directly from nerves into the mechanism of the mechanical appendage. So a replacement arm or leg can be controlled directly through mental control, rather like the Chinese quad-copter only a little more personal. Even more personal, if that's the word, we are beginning to grow body parts. The very first artificial tracheal transplant, where the artificial trachea was made of silicon surrounded with stem cells has been a success. Body parts will eventually be grown in labs from stem cells, no more need for donors. Body parts will be made that will allow those who were formerly disabled, super powers of physical capacity. The world as we know it is changing ferociously fast. The exponential drive of progress is only getting faster. We can only glimpse and science-fantasize about how life will be in fifty years let alone five hundred.

We are on the verge of the next level of supercomputer too, this is also on its way. A whole range of possible mechanisms for its structure are being tested, from chlorophyll from plants through to mono-molecular sheets of carbon interlaced with silicon, graphene or other compounds. The quantum computer is on its way. When the quantum computer lands we may be using hand held computers that have the capacity of modern super-computers, like those possessed by organisations such as NASA. Quantum computers will have speeds of operation that will transcend anything we can conceive. Such computers will be used in every arena of exploration and life from personal to medical and scientific inquiry.

The progress of touch screen computing has been limited by the scarcity of the minerals required to create the screens, and hampered by the strategic politics of who controls these resources. However, a new substance is now available which produces micro-tubules derived from wood waste. From this touch screens, 'metallic' vehicle parts and 'plastic' can all be made. This nano-crystalline cellulose, which is also bio-degradable appears to be totally harmless. We also have the possibility of making silicon-based nano-tubules from sand that can be used in the semiconductor industry. Yet, whether touch screens will become a historic footnote remains to be seen. If direct neural-silicon interfaces become common the human mind could be directly 'wired up' to the world-wide-web. We will be the world-wide-web, with all its vast flows of information, spam and carbon based citta[35] chatter (that's a yoga joke for those who understand Sanskrit terms for aspects of mind).

As for energy production we have phenomenal capacities becoming available through our scientific endeavour. Bio-fuels leader Jonathan Trent is showing the world how to grow as much carbon-neutral fuel as we need. We also have all we need to make electricity through solar concentrating mirrors, that's before we even look to wind-power, geo-thermal, biomass generators, wave power or any other means, as the chapter on energy production considered. The remaining question is why are we still drilling for oil when it is clearly so passé?

Hybrid airplanes have been designed and could be put into production, especially with the new micro-tubule nano-technology, graphene[36], kevlar or other such super substances that can produce lightweight and super-strong fuselages. We could be running this beautiful planet on carbon-neutral energy sources within twenty years - with the right investment and the political will. Yes, we really could!

With the squabbling power hungry tribes and religions of humanity mostly invested with wrapping themselves up in vested beliefs, interests and mediaeval mindsets there's still a long way to go. With self-interested behaviour oriented around personal wealth aggrandisement is still considered as 'the way' of doing business on this beautiful planet. Considering all of this we further understand that there certainly is a long, long way to go. With large corporations and the governments being ruled and dictated by, largely, self-centred interests we have a lot of educational and developmental work to do. We have a good deal of groundwork to do simply to gain access to all the amazing technology that is available, to transform and limit the damaging practices of the present and co-create a future worth living.

Of course the future is always different to our imaginings and the current explorations around graphene point to a carbon-graphene interface of very interesting potential. Whether we like it or not, and here those egoic mindsets of raga, dvesha and moha come back into play, whether we like it or not, the carbon-silicon interface and all it's scary and promising possibilities is not going away. It is simply a choice between paying attention and co-creating the future from the integrity of our

35. Citta is the dynamic vortex of thinking and feeling stuff that comprises the brain activity of a person who has not cultivated an effective practice of mind training.

36. Graphene is a monomolecular fabric of enormous strength, flexibility and potential for information movement that is far from fully understood. Yet!

practice, or hiding our heads under our meditation cushions and hoping for a return to some golden age.

Comedy

The twelfth key-point of conscious evolution is comedy

The capacity to juxtapose opposites in unexpected ways, the way of presenting paradox in comical and accessible form, the means of easing fear and playing with the edges of consensual reality. Comedy is totally awesome. Comedy has been shown to help people who are suffering from depression and to speed healing rates for other illnesses, hence Dr Patch Adams great work with accelerating healing through laughter. The funny thing about comedy is that we all find different things funny, some of us laugh at slapstick and others at quite dark humour. However we do it, comedy works. Comedy works to bring politicians and religious leaders down to size, it resolves the tendency to turn people into demigods. Comedy is, amongst many other things the irreverent antidote to deification.

Higher primates laugh. They laugh to ease social distress and uncertainty; it's a means of resolving social tension. Primates laugh as a way of dispelling fear; laughter and tears are so closely related, as we know. Dolphins appear to laugh; they certainly play and have large enough brains to get the joke of appearing to be separate things. We human beings take ourselves so seriously, and yet when we resolve our illusion of separateness it is humour that arises as a key quality of awakened mind. A Yogi really is known by their laugh! When a Yogin no longer takes the universe personally, when the dualities of existence and impermanence no longer worry such a practitioner, then laughter is the natural response.

Christopher was fortunate to spend a short time with some Vietnamese monks. They spoke little English and he little French. The ninety-four year old monk and the diminutive eighty-year old communicated through resonance and ebullient and infectious laughter.

When our clever minds reach the point where we finally realise that the universe is so much more complex and beautiful than any concept we can throw at it, when we realise that our stunning bio-computers that only work in dualistic conceptual patterning cannot grasp the vastness and intricacy of the cosmos, only then, as we drop out of conceptual mind, can we can begin to see and appreciate the sane responses of total awe, sublime bio-philia and heartfelt laughter. Yes comedy is an evolutionary art. So the twelfth evolutionary art is having a laugh!

Which reminds us, did you hear the one about the Buddha selling hot dogs?

Conflict Resolution

The thirteenth key-point of yoga as conscious evolution is conflict resolution

In human relational events, conflicts happen.

When conflicts happen how do we choose to mediate and resolve them?

In many contemporary schools conflicts are mediated and resolution sought through clear processes of considered action. When bullying and aggression occur the situation is brought to conflict resolution and slowly resolved. Fundamentally, the recognition exists that someone who sources their feel-good factor and esteem by bullying others is unhappy inside.

Meanwhile, some western governments go to war to 'resolve' issues, leading to the death or disablement of thousands of (often innocent) individuals in horrific circumstances. Ironically and consequentially this manifests many more issues for the survivors of such atrocities.

How are we going to co-create a planet where conflict resolution is carried out with clear process and intelligence, not with mindless brutality and weaponry?

Conflict happens, let's accept it, it's totally natural. Waves crash onto rocks wearing the rocks away or smashing them into oblivion. The sun evaporates pools of water and rain dissolves buildings. Antelope eat grass and tigers eat antelopes. Everywhere there is conflict, if we look honestly. Yet if we look every-where then we also find the resolution of conflict.

In human society conflict can be considered to be part of its evolution and development. To date, much conflict escalates into full-blown warfare, obliterating the opportunity for creatively harnessing its energy as a developmental tool is lost, or left to the unconscious vicissitudes and flows of space-time.

Conflict always provides creative and growth opportunities and therefore can be seen as an event that is not inherently negative. It is an arising of energy that can be a powerful force for change if it can be harnessed effectively and worked with towards the end of peace-building. This is the art of conflict management. Conflict in human society is becoming increasingly expensive and a waste of human and other resources. Despite the fact that, historically, war has boosted many failing economies it is a waste of human and ecological resource.

For sure the defence industries initiate a lot of awesome scientific research. The funding could still be there, it doesn't have to be routed through the armaments industry. Some of the current research on robots via the emerging carbon-silicon interface is aimed at creating super robotic warriors.

Sadly it seems that what some of us humans are doing at our current level of development is funding, researching and creating even more effective death machines. To grow out of this mindset and behaviour is an evolutionary project that requires loving dedication and real commitment.

The emerging science of conflict management is a part of this growth. The simple recognition that conflict can be hugely destructive and expensive is at long last making this psychological study viable and worthwhile.

The art of yoga offers key tools for the safe handling of conflict starting with central nervous system management, somatic exploration and awareness of internal dynamics and motivations, as well as ultimately making the self-construct conscious and no longer the driver of our behaviour.

The reduction and management of conflict in other species certainly has evolutionary value. The emerging science of conflict management probably occupies a similar role for us. Either we use conflict creatively through conflict management skills or we create such complex conditions for our own and other species that we head inexorably to extinction.

The Five Limbs of an Integral CRS (conflict resolution system)

- *The cultural creation of personal skills of inner awareness and conflict resolution.*

- *The methods and processes involved in managing the arising energy of conflict, using it creatively and through this prevent the escalation of conflict into all out war*

- *The methods and processes involved in facilitating the end of escalated social conflict or warfare.*

- *Post conflict peace-building.*

- *The methods and processes involved in co-creating a culture that self-regulates for creative conflict management and active peace-building.*

We would love to see this 'Yogic Theory' of conflict resolution in place as a cultural norm.

Understanding the art of communication is key to this development.

As it arises, conflict is usually related to a struggle for autonomy, power or to secure resources for groups or individuals. Co-creating a culture where the 'common ground' is an embedded cultural construct would craft a social environment required to facilitate the above pentagon of conflict resolution skills as a cultural norm.

One of Christopher's sons was at a school in the UK where a degree of conflict resolution using mediation was in place, with relative effect and making a big difference on playground bullying. Such strategies can really work. At the same time the 'adults' in western governments were belligerently going to war in Iraq on what now transpire to be trumped up pretences… What sort of example is this?

What happened to the political leaders (war criminals in need of psychological help?) who created this conflict?

Where are they now?

How was this allowed to happen?

Five Key Strategies of Integral CRS

Five further strategies in conflict resolution and peace-building as an aspect of this (CRS) are important.

• *Consistently re-membering and celebrating the common ground.*

• *Negotiation. Dialogue between involved parties. Involved parties have to believe they get more from dialogue than engaging in escalating conflict.*

• *Compromise. Where involved parties are willing to reduce some part of their demands on resources or others in concern for the common good.*

• *Mediation. Conflict resolution facilitated by a third party who seeks to open and improve dialogue and lead towards any necessary compromise and peace-building. This is a real opportunity for creative use of the energy of conflict to deepen awareness for all and craft social possibilities of deeper mutual engagement and understanding.*

• *Cooperation. Where the balance of the triad of:*

  • *Concern for self*

  • *Concern for others*

  • *Concern for the common good*

…are held so effectively that conflict management and resolution becomes an art.

The strategies of avoidance where parties just hope it will all go away rarely work.

Strategies of yielding to oppressive forces rarely work long-term.

Strategies of competition, seeking to win, rarely work out for the greatest common good where win-win-win is needed.

Conciliation can work, this is where one seeks to regulate conflict through demand accountancy - I'll give up this demand if you give up that one…

So the five skills of the art of CRS are essential in our contemporary world. They are an art form and an art form we would do well to embed within our global culture.

The internalisation practices of yogic awareness are the first limb of this art of CRS.

Many yoga practitioners and spiritual teachers look back into the past to some golden age or another, the Satya Yuga, the land of Ogyen, Atlantis, or whatever it may be for them. Personally we are relatively disinterested in such speculative stories and romantic notions, however delightful. We are, however, deeply interested in the golden age we are co-creating.

What are we crafting in this moment?

This moment is the evolution of the golden age, the age of now, and in this moment and from this moment the age yet to come.

It is conscious evolution and the broad awareness this de-

mands that leads us forward into this moment and all moments. This moment is the open-hearted realisation of complete indivisibility and inseparability that leads us into the new
golden age, the new earth of this moment and all moments.

Yoga is conscious evolution. In yoga we neither look back
in regret or romantic whimsy, nor do we look forward in fear.
We simply look around in appreciative, vast awareness and act
wisely and lovingly from this place and then, in this moment,
exists the golden age.

Slowly we will craft a world where all beings know themselves
as indivisible from each other and will treat each other with
simple kindness, respect, appreciation, interest and even love.

This is the promise of the age of Maitreya, the essence of the
second coming and the nature of Al Mahdi.

This is the work of Engaged Yoga.

Are you ready?

"In the sky, there is no distinction of east and west;
people create distinctions out of their own minds and then believe them to be true."
Buddha

Christopher Gladwell

For more than thirty years I have studied biology, physiology and psychology. My teaching weaves these sciences with traditional yogic and tantric pragmatic philosophy.

This book is a contemporary synergy of my work, and invites you to share in my passion for realising our human potential through yoga and related practices.

I teach in the UK and internationally, and would love to share my work with you.

www.christophergladwell.com

Louise Wender

My approach to photography has no place or need for post-production editing.

Life is already inspiring and powerful.

As well as being a photographer I'm also a qualified psycho-therapist, trainer and facilitator for positive change.

It is through this work and my photography that I enjoy enabling people to achieve joyful well-being in their lives, by seeing and experiencing things from a new perspective.

www.louisewender.com

ENGAGED YOGA

Yoga woven into daily life

Siddha Publishing